THE LAKE SUPERIOR AGATE: FOURTH EDITION

By Scott F. Wolter

Publisher	Scott F. Wolter
Copy Editor	Nancy Baldrica and Janet Wolter
Layout and Design	Jennifer Wreisner
Front Cover Photo	Amanda L. Wolter

ISBN 978-1-60250-123-2 (1-60250-123-8)

Published by Lake Superior Agate Inc.
P.O. Box 14611
Minneapolis, Minnesota 55414
651-659-1345
swolter@amengtest.com
www.lakesuperioragate.com

Printed in the United States
10 9 8 7 6 5 4 3 2 1

DEDICATION

This book is dedicated to my father, Fred Addison Wolter. It's been 25 years now and we miss you, and love you more than ever.

TABLE OF CONTENTS

ACKNOWLEDGEMENTS

After 22 years and four editions, I have many people to thank for their support. It started with Don Harrer with Starr Press, who showed kindness to the kid that had more agates than money back in 1986. Over the years, I have received support from many friends and readers who have been just as fanatical about Lake Superior agates as I have been. Many of these people you will read about here, but a few deserve special mention....

Phil Gotsch is the man who spearheaded the effort for the Moose Lake Agate/Geological Interpretive Center and continues to be an inspiration to the hobby and me!

Todd Hosteger has been working on me for years to co-author a book on agates of the world. His passion for agates is unrivaled, and if it weren't for Johann Zenz, who beat us to the punch in 2005, Todd and I would no doubt be fully engrossed in the project. I want to thank Todd for his continual and enthusiastic support.

John Marshall is a lifelong collector of Lakers who somehow ended up in Oregon instead of Minnesota. In spite of the geographic challenges, he provides strong support for my work with agates and the hobby in general.

Mike Carlson is another great friend and ambassador for the hobby. He's seen many great agates of all types, but he's always said that Lakers were the best.

Bruce Peddle is one of the primary agate "boys" who I've spent many hours with "skonging" stone. He and his wife, Kim, have been great friends for a long time.

Charlie White is one of those collectors who keeps a low profile, but has a fervent enthusiasm for the hobby. He has a tremendous collection and isn't afraid to make deals that most other collectors wouldn't have the stomach for. Charlie has provided a lot of input to this edition, and I thank him for his critical advice, friendship, and support.

Janet, Grant, and Amanda Wolter have been my constant supporters, even when I go a little overboard. They've sat both in the car for hundreds of hours while I chased after agates and behind the table at numerous rock shows every year listening to me spin my yarns and pitch sales. I especially want to thank them for their unwavering love and support!

PREFACE

Wow! It's hard to believe that I'm sitting here writing the introduction to yet another edition of that little book I put together about my favorite rock twenty-one years ago. I never could have dreamed back then how—through incredible timing and great luck—we would sell over 25 thousand copies and still have enough interest in the book to warrant writing a fourth edition. The first edition of this book was published in 1986, and the response was a very pleasant surprise. What started out as project to help me heal from a great loss (my father died in a 1983 scuba diving accident) and to share my passion for agates with others, met and exceeded all expectations. I extend my appreciation and thanks to all who laid out their hard-earned dollars to read about Lake Superior Agates. In the summer of 1993, when the second printing sold out, I was content to let it end on a successful note. I thought that the agate story had been told, and even though the book was still selling, maybe it was time to move on. The book's retirement didn't last long.

I was approached about selling the rights to a publisher and letting them take over the day-to-day routine of selling books. The more I thought about it, the better the idea sounded. After meeting with Jon Earl at Burgess Publishing, I quickly became excited about what could be done to improve the book. As our discussions continued, the ideas began to snowball. We decided to add more photos to the portfolio, replace existing photos, and add what we hoped would be some interesting additional reading. The Second Edition of the Lake Superior Agate came out in 1994, and people bought it just as quickly as the first book. By 1996, the books were gone again, and I was ready to do a Third Edition. Again, we did the book with Jon Earl, only this time, with his new company, Outernet Publishing. The amazing run of selling agate books has continued, and in the summer of 2007, the last books of the Third Edition were gone, with a total of over 25 thousand copies sold for all three editions.

This time, I have no illusions of letting the book die out. I've decided to do a Fourth Edition with a healthy dose of fresh material and a batch of new photos of gorgeous specimens. I'm still going to include much of the original material for old time's sake, but the new stories, photos, and information will make this edition appealing to all those who bought the earlier editions. This book marks the end of doing agate books with Jon Earl, though we remain good friends. The business of publishing books has changed dramatically; it is now cheaper and easier to make books using on-demand publishing houses. Jon and I had a great run for 14 years, and I am very grateful for his friendship and support!

Some people wonder if there is anything more to write about with Lake Superior Agates; the answer is a resounding, "Absolutely!" I am happy to report that the hobby is more popular than ever, and the supply of Lakers that the earth gives up shows no signs of slowing in the foreseeable future.

Construction has accelerated, along with the increasing need for glacial aggregate for concrete, asphalt, landscaping, and other uses. This has increased the number of new gravel pits and the production of material in existing pits. These havens for agate pickers have produced some fabulous new agates, but the news is not all good on this front. Liability concerns by pit owners are leading to restricted access to these hunting grounds at an accelerating pace. Clashes between pit owners and eager agate collectors are becoming more frequent. I am hopeful that a compromise can be worked out. One idea is to pursue a state-supported agate-picking license for collectors. However, until a resolution to the problem is reached, collectors must remember not to trespass onto private property. If an area does hold promise for agates, the best chance for a successful experience is to use a tried-and-true approach: respectfully ask for permission.

INTRODUCTION

This book is about a hobby that people of all ages can enjoy. The hobby offers a chance to get outdoors, get some exercise, and collect something of value. The best part is all of this is free. The hobby is collecting specimens of a beautiful and special stone, the Lake Superior agate – Minnesota's state gemstone. Anyone who has ever seen a Lake Superior agate is aware of the beauty of these gemstones, but not everyone is aware of how special these stones really are.

Agates are found in many areas of the United States and around the world, but the Lake Superior agate is unique. First, it is the oldest of all the agates found around the globe. Its formation dates back over 1 billion years. It is also unique in that it originates in an area that is rich in iron, a pigment in rocks that provides a wide array of color.

In addition, the most recent agents to act upon the precious gemstones were the vast glaciers of the Great Ice Age, which spread the agates over a large, accessible hunting ground while opening them up during transport to expose their internal beauty. Lake Superior agates are found in glacial deposits ranging from the shores of Lake Superior to as far south as Topeka, Kansas.

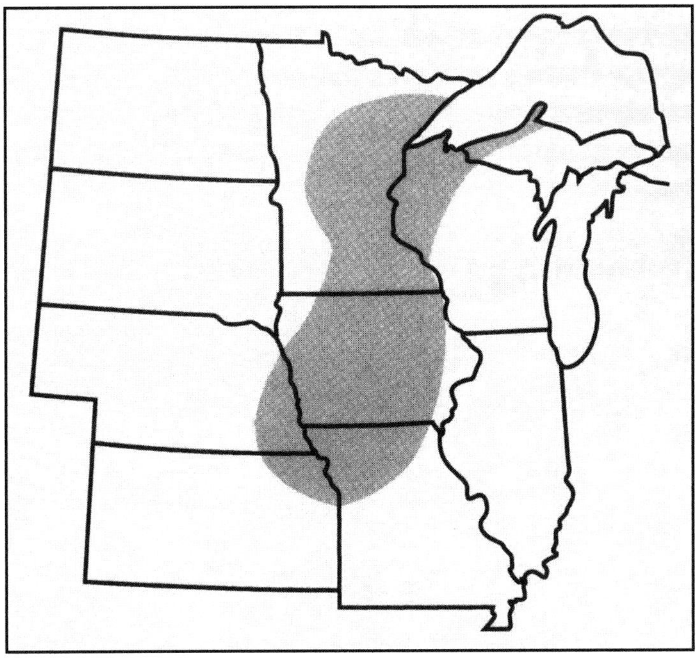

Figure I-1: the light gray area on the map indicates the approximate area of distribution of Lake Superior agates found in glacial deposits.

Collecting Lake Superior agates is not only a physically and intellectually challenging pastime, but it can also be a profitable activity. The agates can be sold as lapidary material for tumbling, cutting, and polishing, or sold in their natural state as specimen pieces. Some especially beautiful specimens, such as many of those pictured in the portfolio, are worth hundreds and sometimes thousands of dollars to collectors.

It is easy for almost anyone to become excited about the beauty of these stones, but the real rewards of the hobby are most available to people who know something about agates. This book was written as an introduction for the beginning collector and as a supplemental resource for the more experienced collector. The book therefore not only provides tips on how and where to look for agates, but also describes types of agates and their features, presents brief histories of agate formation and collecting, and provides information on how agates may be cut or treated to enhance their natural beauty. In addition, I have included several short essays on my own and other collector's personal experiences that I hope will give the reader a feeling of what to expect from the hobby.

If the lure of a hobby is in setting a goal and attaining it, then it is hard for me to explain why more people aren't agate hunters. There is nothing quite like the feeling of searching for a beautiful Lake Superior agate and finding one! I hope this book will encourage more people to share the enjoyment this activity has given me, as well as help those who already enjoy collecting agates. I do have to leave one last thought for beginners before they start reading, just so they can't say they weren't warned: Proceed at your own risk. Once the agate bug bites, its effects can last a lifetime.

CHAPTER 1
A Brief History of Lake Superior Agate Collecting

Since human beings have always been intrigued by the idea of finding beautiful and valuable minerals, such as gold and diamonds, it should not be surprising that the search for the beautiful (if somewhat less valuable) agate has also had a considerable history. Although most the documentation of that history is informal, consisting of stories, theories, and educated guesses, the proof is in the agate collections. In many collections throughout Lake Superior agate country, hundreds of specimens, both large and small, were not found by their present owners. Many larger specimens have been traded and sold, often many times, throughout the last 100 years and perhaps longer. Special agates have been passed on from one generation to another, as family heirlooms. Other agates have remained at the surface, often within plain sight, for many years before their accidental discovery. If each gemstone could speak, every story would be a different as the individual stone themselves.

We do not know who first saw a Lake Superior agate, or when, but it probably happened shortly after human beings entered North America for the first time, soon after the great glaciers retreated. Between 12,000 to 11,000 years ago, (the dates are derived from Carbon-14 dating of fossil campfires believed used by early North Americans) the Cordilleran ice sheet to the west and the Laurentide ice sheet to the east opened an ice-free corridor that led prehistoric man into what is now the United States (Figure 1-1).

Although there is no documented evidence, it is likely that early Native Americans may have considered Lake Superior agates sacred and used them for decoration, trade and as ceremonial objects. The Minnehaha Falls agate is one prominent example of a spectacular large Laker that Natives certainly held in high regard. (See essay: The Minnehaha Falls Agate, page 89). I have personally seen a one-pound agate belonging to a member of the Lakota tribe that suggests what early technology might have been able to do with agates. The owner's grandson told me how his grandfather had cut the stone with rope and hand-polished the face with fine sand and water. The process must have been time-consuming, but the finished product was of high quality.

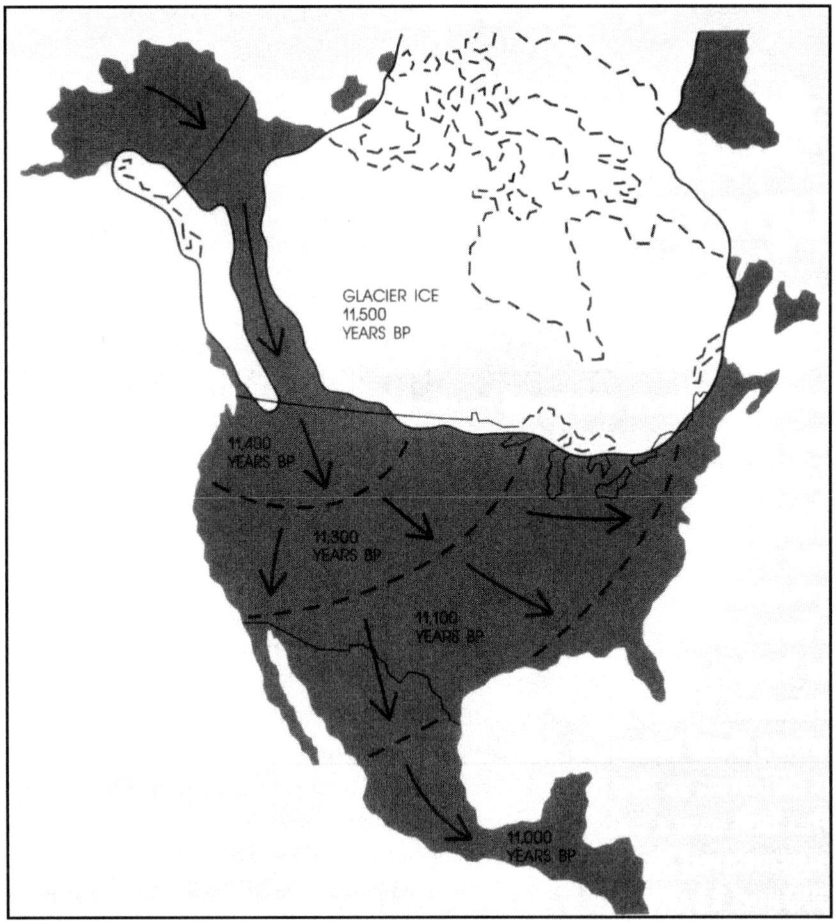

Figure 1-1: Early man likely migrated into North America across the Bering Straight land bridge and then moved south between the steadily retreating Laurentide and Cordilleran ice sheets along the route indicated by the arrows. Numbers are years before the present (B.P.).

Settlers of European stock, who began moving into Minnesota and Wisconsin about 1800, are the first recorded collectors of Lake Superior agates. The first generally recognized description of the Lake Superior agate was made by Henry Rowe Schoolcraft in 1820. Schoolcraft made his observations during his tenure as chief geologist of two expeditions into the Lake Superior region, in 1820 and again in 1832. The land around Fort Snelling was opened to legal settlement in 1837 and in 1858 Minnesota became a state, two events that encouraged an increase in population and thus in the potential number of agate collectors.

These early settlers were often engaged in work that brought them into contact with agates, but they were likely to consider rocks as obstacles rather than objects of interest. The first farmers had to deal with virgin glacial debris. Even after clearing the land of timber, they were confronted by fields covered with a seemingly endless number of boulders and smaller rocks. As these pioneers laboriously removed the stones by hand, most of the agates were dumped in piles of rocks, gullies and other out-the-way places. These early rock piles later yielded many fine gems that initially went undetected. Occasionally, however, a rock was so different from the others that it caught the farmer's eye. The earliest collectors recognized these banded beauties as something special and saved them. By the early 1890s, several northern Minnesota families had small collections of agates they had found on their property. A few of the more serious collectors began venturing off their own land in search of new sources of agates.

Around 1900, a lapidary industry began on Michigan's Keweenaw Peninsula. This local agate industry produced tiny, polished agates that were drilled to make beads. Many Lake Superior agates were cut into marbles, and some of these antique marbles may still be seen in private collections on display at antique and gem shows.

Throughout the first 30 years of this century, the hobby of agate collecting and lapidary grew with the increase in population and the exposure of more areas to agate hunting. A retired farmer/rockhound from the Milaca, Minnesota area recalled his days picking rocks during the Great Depression. Richard Sundeen's farm must have been a relative goldmine for agates. *"We must have dumped many agates off the wagon and into the river,"* he related. *"There were so many rocks, it would have been easier to remove the dirt."*

As construction increased in response to the steady rise in population, so did the demand for concrete, and the sand and aggregate used in it. Sand and gravel deposits are virtually endless in the glacially constructed topography of the area and, consequently, gravel pits became more numerous. These gravel pits were ideal places to look for large agates because in them rocks were mechanically sorted by size. Gravel-sorting machines separated out the agates from the depths of the overburden into neat piles, ripe for picking. While this new technology concentrated large, beautiful agates in relative abundance, it may also have triggered a very unfortunate and disturbing practice.

Portable gravel sorters are an agate collector's dream. Front-end loaders drop unsorted material by the ton through the screen at right onto a conveyor belt. Sand and gravel are then carried up to a series of vibrating screens that separate the rocks into size-graded piles.

In the late 1930s, many collectors began sawing large agates (weighing a pound or more) in half to uncover their hidden beauty. A person who had come across a large agate would bring it to somebody with a diamond saw and have it cut in two, giving the cutter one of the halves. Apparently, this practice was commonplace throughout the 1940s and 1950s, until big agates became increasingly scarce. Perhaps many collectors thought that the gravel sorters would produce quantities of large agates forever. Word soon spread, however, that "sawing for halves" was depleting the number of these treasured finds, and the practice all but stopped.

The ambitious highway projects that began after World War II created a "Gold Rush" period for the Lake Superior agate. The major overhaul of the country's road system and the massive interstate highway building included projects in Minnesota and Wisconsin. As new roads were constructed, more agates were discovered. Preliminary bulldozing and grading of virgin countryside frequently exposed soils packed with agates. Many collectors remember these projects, and tell of how they patiently waited for rain after construction work.

Harold Johnston of Rice Lake, Wisconsin, who began collecting agates in 1922 at the age of 6, remembers what he calls "those unbelievable days." He recalled one particular day when, after a rainfall of several inches, he collected a 5-gallon bucket full of agates just by walking along a bulldozed tract that was to be a railroad bed. The combination of the construction work and the rain had left the stones perfectly exposed.

Not only did the highway construction projects expose agates, but activity within the gravel pits was also in full swing during this period. The increased activity to provide sand and both sorted and unsorted gravel for concrete and base material also exposed hordes of agates. Many fine gems were discovered during these busy times.

In 1950, the late Theodore Vanasse of Spring valley, Wisconsin, published the first edition of his book *Lake Superior Agate*. Mr. Vanasse, a quiet, humble man, also owned an agate museum where he displayed all the agates pictured in his book, although now decades out of print, is well-written and was for a long time the Lake Superior agate collector's bible.

Agate collecting and lapidary in general reached its peak in the late 1950s and early 1960s. Many fine collections of

The beautiful 2.15-pound red and white Lake Superior agate on portfolio page C15 was found by Rudolph Halderson (standing next to his son Raymond at right in this circa 1939 picture taken overlooking Duluth, Minnesota) when he worked on the Sawbill Trail near Grand Marais, Minnesota, as part of the Civilian Conservation Corp government projects in the early 1930s. (Photograph courtesy of Karl Halderson) In October of 2007, Willie Thomson (pictured with his girlfriend Jessica) found the 11.15-pound monster in his hands only two weeks before.

large Lake Superior agates were amassed in Minnesota and Wisconsin. The late George Flaim of Duluth at one time owned more than 300 gem-quality Lake Superior agates weighting over a one pound each. Maynard Green of Grand Meadow started his collection in 1955 by buying the collection of a retired mail carrier. The mail carrier had an original method for collecting agates: children along his route would put agates in their mailboxes, and in return he would leave coins. The bigger the agate, the bigger the coin! After Mr. Green bought the collection, he added to it by making several trips throughout Minnesota each year, buying agates from other collectors. By the early 1980s when I met Maynard, his house was filled with agates. At that time he had probably the largest number of gem-quality "Lakers" in a single collection. Maynard has since sold his collection, but his eyes still light up when someone shows him a good big one.

In the summer of 1969, the Lake Superior agate received its highest honor when it was named the official Minnesota State gemstone. In the 1970s, however, a general slowdown occurred in the hobby. Conversations with some of the older collectors suggest several possible reasons for the slowdown. First, many of the older collectors have died, and younger people are not filling the void. Interest in rocks, and outdoor hobbies in general, seemed to be declining to some extent. Faster-paced lifestyles may have limited the amount of free time available to people. Agate collecting and lapidary are both time-consuming hobbies, and lapidary equipment, especially, can be expensive.

In addition, the number of areas in which to find agates seems to be decreasing. Although some gravel pits are still processing gravel and producing agates, the older gravel-sorting machines have been replaced by a new machine called the "crusher." The crusher pulverizes rocks into the small diameter particles by the pit operators, regardless of the stones' initial size or beauty. Lake Superior agates are no exception. It is also more difficult to get permission to search for agates in gravel pits because of the owners concern about liability. Still, in spite of these drawbacks, agate collecting has flourished. In the 1980s the hobby gained a new popularity. From my perspective, it seems that Lake Superior agate collecting activity increased shortly after the first edition of this book came out in November of 1986. At the time it was published, there was very little about Lake Superior agates to read. There were a few older articles in the monthly magazine Lapidary Journal and Ted Vanasse's book, but it had been out of print for over 30 years. The timing for a new book was right. Old passions for agates were rekindled, and new ones were ignited.

A large rock crusher reduces rocks into fragments of a preferred diameter. It is anyone's guess how many big, beautiful Lake Superior agates have been broken into small pieces by machines like this in the last few decades.

In May of 1987, my longtime picking partner, Mike Carlson, and I organized an agate extravaganza. We called it the "Night of the Lake Superior Agates". We reserved a gymnasium in Northeast Minneapolis for the event. Flyers were sent out to rock clubs all over Minnesota and Wisconsin to invite people to display their collections. On the day of the show, my wife Janet and I invited several collector friends to our house for an agate preview and picnic. It was a hot, sunny day, and I'll never forget all the choice agates spread out over our lawn. Collectors from Nebraska, Missouri, Wisconsin and Minnesota were there. It looked like a flea market for rocks. I can't help but wonder what my neighbors thought. By late afternoon the agates were packed up and Mike and I led a caravan through Minneapolis to the show. Display cases were set up around the perimeter of the gym, all crammed with beautiful Lakers. The festivities included a slide program I put together on agates and Mike read a letter from then Governor Rudy Perpich congratulating us on the show.

It seemed like from that night on, the mad scramble for trophy Lakers was on. I was in the gravel pits more than ever looking for agates the next three summers, but so was everyone else! During this time, an increasing number of collectors appeared trying to buy agates. I was right in the middle of it. Prices began to soar. It didn't take long and the price for choice large specimens reached $100 a pound and occasionally more! The spiraling inflation may have put a strain on the pocketbook, but it also brought many older agates out of the closet. Many of those beauties collected during the "days of frenzy" are pictured throughout this book.

In 1997, Mike and I decided to have a ten-year anniversary and along with fellow agate fanatic Reverend Phil Gotsch, we organized and held the "Night of the Lake Superior Agate 2" at the St. Philip's Lutheran Church in Fridley, Minnesota. Once again there were cases of beautiful agates lining the sanctuary with many familiar faces and several new ones as well. Although Phil, Mike and I considered having another extravaganza on the 20th anniversary of the first get-together, we settled instead on savoring a different event that will benefit agate collectors and rock-hounds far into the future. On July 19, 2003, Phil Gotsch's idea to build an interpretive center to tell the story of Minnesota's geology and the Lake Superior agate came true after seventeen years of persistence. Phil, myself, Minnesota State Representatives Mary Murphy, Bill Hilty and Becky Lourey, Park Superintendent Don Del Greco and Minnesota DNR Head of the Parks Division Bill Morressey cut the ribbon at the entrance to a beautiful 1.4 million dollar building at Moose Lake State Park.

There were many happy faces at the ribbon-cutting ceremony for the dedication of the Agate/Geological Interpretive Center in Moose Lake, Minnesota, on July 19, 2003. L to R: Reverend Phil Gotsch, Scott Wolter, Amanda Wolter, Representatives Mary Murphy and Bill Hilty, Don Del Greco and Representative Becky Lourey.

It's a fantastic building that has 4000 square foot room filled with displays of agates and interpretive material about Minnesota's geological history that includes how agates were formed. The facility has a classroom, gift shop, park administration offices and first class rest rooms. I am proud to have been an early participant to help see Phil's dream come true. This facility is a wonderful destination for agate collectors from around the world to learn and celebrate what is arguably the most beautiful agate type in the world.

Another sign of the resurgence in the agate hobby is the publication of several books by authors in the Lake Superior region. My good friend and long-time collector John Marshall wrote a book in 2006 about the often overlooked varieties of Lakers other than the well-banded fortification type. *"The Other Lake Superior Agates"* includes many stunning photographs that bring well-deserved attention to the lesser appreciated agate types such as waterlevels, sagenites, mosaic and many others. In 2002, Mike Carlson put together arguably one of the most visually stunning books ever on agates entitled *"The Beauty of Banded Agates: An Exploration of Agates from Eight Major Worldwide Sites."* Of course one of those sites is our very own Lake Superior region. Mike's "coffee table" style book includes hundreds of amazing colors photographs of both rough specimens and incredible examples of lapidary. Even yours truly wrote another book entitled, *"The Lake Superior: One Man's Journey"* in 2001. That book is part an autobiography and part historical summary of the characters in the hobby and the incredible agates they collected through the period of the 1980s thorough 2000. Another book that deserves mention was first published in 1998 and is now in its second edition (2002). Roger Clark's *"Fairburn Agate: Gem of South Dakota"* brought world-wide attention to a beautiful agate type that in many ways resembles Lake Superior agates in its rough state. Roger said he was inspired to write his book in part after reading the first edition of this book. Several other excellent books about agates found throughout the world have appeared in the last decade.

Several new books about agates have been published in the last few years. Authors John Marshall (2006), Roger Clark (2002), Michael Carlson (2002), and yours truly (2001) wrote the titles pictured here.

In spite of what some people think, there are still countless agates yet to be discovered within glacial debris, and the gems will continue to be exposed in many different ways. Over the twenty-seven years that I have been collecting and purchasing agates, I've seen more large, high-quality specimens coming out of the ground in the last half-dozen years than ever before. This means there are definitely agates out there to be found, the problem is it's getting tougher to get into gravel pits without trespassing. Phil Gotsch and I are currently working with State officials on the possibility of "rock-hound license" for agate collectors. We believe a compromise can be reached with private gravel pit operators across the state of Minnesota where responsible collectors can pursue their hobby in the best place to find their treasures. We may never see the "Gold Rush" days of agate collecting again, or at least not for some time, by with a little imagination, logical thinking, and luck, collecting Lake Superior agates can be an enjoyable and rewarding hobby for years to come.

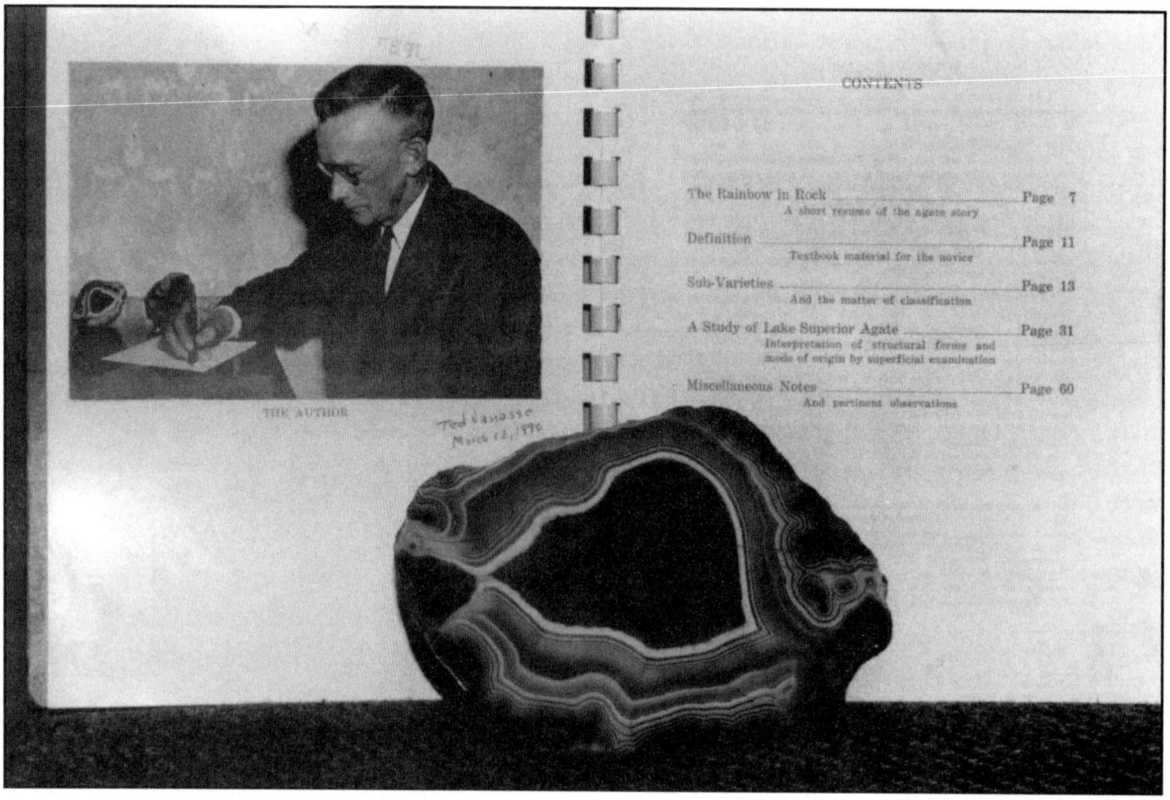

The Other Half: A stunning red and white Laker, weighing roughly three pounds, was cut in half and polished sometime before 1950. The sister half of this gem can be seen in the photograph with Mr. Theodore Vanasse. He book, *Lake Superior Agate*, was first published in 1948.

Essay: Newton Winchell's Agate

I've long wondered what the Native Americans in Minnesota did with the Lake Superior agates they no-doubt found in the years prior to settlement. They certainly revered agates as much as many of us do now, and perhaps held them sacred. The Minnehaha Falls agate, named after the highly sacred place where it was found, is the most obvious example. Another question that has puzzled my brain is what happened to the many specimens the Native Americans must have collected? I found the answer to where many of the agates ended up while performing research for a book I co-wrote about a long-festering Minnesota mystery called the Kensington Rune Stone. A pleasant realization occurred when I learned that the highly respected geologist Newton Winchell, the first State geologist of Minnesota in 1877, had performed a geologic study of the artifact. (Winchell also concluded it was genuine.)

Among his many contributions to the geologic history of Minnesota was a prestigious book published in 1911 by the Minnesota Historical Society entitled *"The Aborigines of Minnesota."* Winchell was recruited by the Society to complete this important book after the original researcher and intended author, J. B. Brower, died of a stroke in 1905. Brower would have been proud of the job Winchell did.

While reading the book, I found several citations of the contents uncovered during the excavation of Indian grave mounds in the latter part of the 1800s. In addition to common burial items entombed with the deceased, time and again, they found Lake Superior agates among the grave goods. That Natives included agates among their burial items indicates how important these gems were in their culture. While paging through Winchell's tome, I came upon a photograph of dozens of arrowheads made out of various rock types. In the bottom row, I spotted the familiar banding pattern that was labeled *"Agate."* My curiosity was piqued, and I decided to see if I could find it.

In January of 2004, I made an appointment to look through the Brower Collection of Native American artifacts at the Minnesota Historical Society archives at the History Center in St. Paul. The collection was located four floors below ground level and, after getting out of the elevator, I was led to an examination room. Dan Cagley wheeled several cardboard boxes into the room on a cart. The boxes were filled with plastic bags full of artifacts. The artifacts included axes, hammers, arrowheads, pottery, and several metal tools made of iron and copper. Each artifact was labeled with a catalog number that corresponded to a location and date the artifact was collected. Several of the bags contained Lake Superior agates that were described in Winchell's book. I spent three days going through the artifacts and, on the last day, I found what I was looking for. Inside a Ziplock bag of small arrowheads was a brightly colored, orange and white "bird" point that looked familiar. It was the very same Lake Superior agate arrowhead pictured in Winchell's book!

This Lake Superior agate arrowhead (left) was pictured on page 416 of the book *"The Aborigines of Minnesota"* by Newton H. Winchell, written in 1911. I found the very same agate arrowhead in the J. B. Brower collection of Native American artifacts in the archives of the Minnesota Historical Society at the History Center in St. Paul on January 22, 2004 (see portfolio page C-5).

Essay: Two Special Agates

All collectors of Lake Superior agates have certain days that remain etched in their minds. Particular specimens in their collection from the largest agate they ever found to the most beautiful are reminders of those special days. Another special day for collectors is the day they found their first agate. I know the day I found my first agate remains clear in my mind, and like any other collector, I have memories of several special agates.

I found my first agate in the place many people automatically think of when they hear about the Lake Superior agate- along the North Shore of the big lake. It was the spring of 1981, my senior year at the University of Minnesota-Duluth. We were on a weekend field trip to Lake Superior for a glacial geology class. The instructor was a professor and geologist named Charles L. Matsch, whom we affectionately called Charlie. Besides being knowledgeable and intelligent, Charlie possesses an even more important set of attributes for a teacher: he inspires enthusiasm, curiosity, and wonder in his students. In addition, he has an incredible wit, which he uses to good effect in his teaching.

Approximately 30 students piled into a caravan of cars and headed north along the shore in Charlie's wake. Between Duluth and Two Harbors, Charlie pulled his car over to the side of the road. We climbed out of our cars and followed him down a short trail to the edge of the lake, where a steep, wave-eroded bank exposed a considerable layer of stony, reddish-brown, glacial sediment. Charlie told each of us to dig into the sediment and retrieve the first stone we found. We were then to reassemble with our finds for a "pebble count," an exercise to determine, by the type of stones we collected, what path the glacier took and where it originated. Charlie signaled us to begin digging and away we went.

The first rock I found was about the size of a cherry. After wiping off the red clay, I noticed lines running through the stone. I quickly became frustrated, because although I had a basic knowledge of the area's various rock types, I didn't know what type of rock I had found. I showed Charlie the stone and as he studied it, he smiled. He then moved to the edge of the lake and washed off the remaining clay in its chilly water. He showed me the rock again, and the lines were everywhere, displaying a beautiful pattern I had never seen before. Charlie then told me that I had found "a Lake Superior agate, the Minnesota state gemstone." Little did I know that this small stone would spark a lifelong passion.

While that first stone was special, recalling another agate inspires an even broader smile and deeper feelings. I found it while hunting agates on a day off from my first job as a geologist, which Charlie helped me get. That particular agate weighed about 1/2 pound and I considered it an especially beautiful one. I thought about Charlie and all he had done for me and decided to give it to him. It was a small way to say "thanks," but I think he appreciated it.

Two years after I gave him that agate, I had a new job, again thanks in part to Charlie, and my love affair with agates was more intense than ever. One day I called Charlie and he told me about his recent expedition to Antarctica, where his research party was only 250 miles from the South Pole. We discussed how frustrating it was to be that close to such a special place, rather like climbing Mount Everest and stopping just short of the top. But, he said, he got a chance to relieve that frustration when a supply plane that was leaving their camp and stopping at the South Pole station offered to take four passengers along for the ride. The 20 or so scientists in camp held a lottery, and he got the fourth seat! Even though the plane would only stop for a few minutes, it was the opportunity of a lifetime.

As luck would have it, Charlie was unable to go because he had to leave camp on a scientific trek on the Antarctic ice sheet the day the plane left. He had planned ahead, however, asking the geophysicist who took his place on the plane to do him a favor. The favor was to take a rock from Minnesota to the Pole, and bury it in the snow. The rock was a Lake Superior agate, the one I had given Charlie two years before. On a note attached to the agate, he wrote, *"With Love from the Superior Lobe."* True to form, Charlie had added that personal touch.

These two agates are especially dear to me, the first one found along the shore of the gem's namesake, and my gift to Charlie, now buried at the South Pole as his gift to the greatest mass of ice in the world. I'll never see that agate again, but you can be sure I'll never forget it.

Charles L. Matsch enjoys tea time at Camp University of Minnesota-Duluth (UMD) in the Sentinel range of the Ellsworth Mountains, West Antarctica (approximately 850 miles from the South Pole). Photograph by Richard W. Ojakangas.

Essay: Those Who Came Before Us

It has now been twenty-seven years since I began collecting Lake Superior agates in earnest. Along the way, I've met many interesting people who were just as passionate about agates as I was, and who had been collecting for a lot longer time. Many of these folks have passed on, leaving huge voids in the hobby. Fortunately, there are many new collectors who have stepped in to fill the void to keep this wonderful hobby alive and healthy. However, I feel it is appropriate to acknowledge the contributions of a few of the individuals no longer with us who had a big impact on me personally, and on the hobby itself in totality.

Rocky Quinn – I first met Rocky in 1981, when I stopped into his shop in Beaver Bay on the North Shore of Lake Superior. He had a museum room filled with amazing rocks and minerals, including two large cases of both polished and rough Lakers. They were the biggest agates I'd ever seen at the time, and they helped me understand very early how big agates could get. Rocky was very friendly and told fun stories about agate collecting, going back to the 1930s. For more than 50 years, he operated the Beaver Bay Agate Shop, which is now owned by Keith and Theresa Bartell. The Agate Shop continues to be open to the public and still has the incredible museum.

This circa 1960 picture is the Beaver Bay Agate Shop, located along the North Shore of Lake Superior in Beaver Bay, Minnesota. Rocky Quinn operated this shop for more than 50 years and likely saw many big and beautiful agates come through during that time.

Ted Vanasse – Ted was one of the first long-time agate collectors I met after the agate bug bit me. The first time I visited him in 1985, he gave me a copy of his 1949 book, *"Lake Superior Agate,"* and then a tour of his agate museum at his home in Spring Valley, Wisconsin. He was a soft-spoken, humble man who deserves credit for writing the first book on Lake Superior agates, which included his classification and description of more than 20 different types.

Ted Vanasse (left) showed off a wooly mammoth tusk when I visited him in Spring Valley, Wisconsin, in 1985. Albert Peterson (right) proudly holds a six-pound Lake Superior agate in front of his service station outside Foley, Minnesota, in 1988.

Albert Peterson – For decades, in the town of Foley, Minnesota, a real character ran a gas station that also included an agate museum on the edge of town. I first visited Albert in 1984, when he gave me a tour of a room behind the station lined with glass cases filled with agates of all types. His favorites were Lake Superior agates, and he had hundreds of them. He told me he assembled his collection by trading gasoline for agates with local farmers who found the stones in their fields.

Harold Johnston – Harold Johnston was the consummate collector. He had a building next to his home in Rice Lake, Wisconsin, literally filled with rocks and minerals. Harold was passionate about all rocks, but had a soft spot for Lake Superior agates, assembling a massive collection over his lifetime. At one time, he probably had the finest collection of large Lake Superior agates, including famous agates like the "Ham," "Buhl Mine," "Foundation," "Candy Striper," and the "Cover Agate," which appeared on the cover of the first edition of this book.

Bruce Peddle (left) poses with Harold Johnston during a visit with him at Rice Lake, Wisconsin, in the late 1980s. John Kammerer and Janet Wolter (below) took a moment for a photo during a visit to his North Minneapolis home in 1989.

John Kammerer – John was in his eighties when I first met him 1983 and he invited me over to his north Minneapolis home. He had collected agates and Native American artifacts since he was a boy, with the fruit of his days in the field prominently displayed throughout his basement. He explained his method of getting a high-quality polish with his tumblers, which were churning away as his spoke. John had a unique way of displaying his tumbled beauties by gluing them onto wood or cardboard, with text written in his beautiful penmanship. What he seemed the most proud of, though, was his collection of Burma Shave signs that he painted for the company when he was a young man. John was very supportive when I wrote my first agate book, and I'll always be grateful for that.

John Moin (1939-2006) – In the spring of 1984, I stopped at the Lignell Drugstore in Superior, Wisconsin, to meet a man who collected Lake Superior agates. John was a calm, easy-going guy who loved to buy, sell, and trade specimens with other collectors. Not only did I and many other collectors acquire some beautiful Lakers from John over the years, but it was he who suggested I stop at a taxidermy shop in Duluth to meet another serious agate collector. That collector was George Flaim, who would have a profound impact on my life and the Lake Superior agate hobby.

Bill Boltz and his wife, Helen, (photo at right) invited Janet, Mike Carlson, and me to see their collection of Lake Superior agates found in Topeka, Kansas, during my trip to Kansas in 1990. John Moin (inset photo) was kind gentleman who collected Lake Superior agates in and around Duluth, Minnesota, for more than 40 years.

Bill Boltz – Meeting Bill Boltz at his home in Topeka, Kansas, in 1990 was a watershed moment, as I saw first-hand the extent of distribution of Lake Superior Agates. The agates he collected in the Topeka area were impressive, indeed, and many can now be seen displayed proudly at the Agate/Geological Interpretive Center in Moose Lake. (See page 45 for the essay: The Boltz Agates.)

Tom Olson – I bought my first big agate from Tom at the 1984 Moose Lake Agate Days show. I named the 2.50-pound rock the "Patriotic Agate" because of its bold red, white, and blue banding. Tom, who passed away in 2004, deserves a lot of credit for being one of the founders of the tremendously successful Moose Lake show, which celebrated its 39th year in 2007. Tom also played an important role, along with Jean Dahlberg, in lobbying at the Capitol for the Lake Superior agate to be officially named the Minnesota State Gemstone in 1969.

Carol Risdon and Tom Olson (above) hold two monster Lake Superior agates during the ground-breaking festivities for the Agate/Geological Interpretive Center in Moose Lake, Minnesota, on a cold April 6, 2002. If there is ever a Lake Superior agate collectors Hall of Fame, George Flaim (right) of Duluth, Minnesota, would be the first inductee. For more than 35 years, he inspired many agate enthusiasts with his colorful tales and remarkable specimens.

George Flaim (1922-2001) – I wrote a chapter in my book, *"The Lake Superior Agate: One Man's Journey,"* about my mentor and close friend, George Flaim, who was not only a legendary Lake Superior agate collector, but an amazing war hero as well. That book is worth getting just to read about George's experience in the South Pacific during World War II. He was not unlike many other heroes from that war, who rarely talked about their experiences. I felt it was important to document some of what he experienced, lest it be lost to history, and his incredible contributions forgotten. We all owe soldiers of today and veterans of past wars our ever-lasting gratitude for their service to our country.

These collectors had a tremendously positive impact on many individuals who enjoy the Lake Superior agate hobby today. I, for one, owe a great deal of gratitude to all these men who shared their time, experience, and incredible specimens that served to mentor and inspire me. At some point, I think there should be a Lake Superior Agate Hall of Fame. Perhaps there could be plaques on the walls at the Moose Lake Agate/Geological Interpretive Center honoring the pioneers of this wonderful hobby. If the day comes when an inaugural class is inducted, many of these names will be there.

CHAPTER 2
Clues to Finding Lake Superior Agates

Once you have decided to try prospecting for agates, what do you look for? There is no simple answer to this question, since there are as many ways to hunt for agates and there are agate hunters. Often, attractively colored or banded agates will be well exposed and easy to find. Most agates however, are not well exposed; only a fraction of the gemstone will be visible to offer a clue to its presence. Probably the single most important factor in agate hunting is luck, the one factor that cannot be controlled.

You can, however, control other important aspects of your search, and thus increase your chances of finding agates, by developing persistence, thoroughness, and a positive attitude. Remember, too, that experience will help sharpen your eye for agates. Before beginning to get this experience, however, you need to know what to look for. The following characteristics will help you identify agates in the field.

Banding is the most obvious clue to look for when identifying agates. Nearly everyone is familiar with the characteristic bands of color in these stones. A feature called "peeled" texture, because it appears as though the bands were peeled off like a banana skin, can be very helpful. The smooth, exposed band planes, along which the agate has fractured or broken, are sometimes readily visible in dirty, poorly exposed rocks.

Too often, however, banding is the only feature that many people look for. Although it is the most obvious characteristic for identifying exposed gemstones, agate hunters who rely on this clue alone are likely to miss many valuable stones. Using other features together with banding will help you find poorly exposed agates that you would otherwise miss.

Color is another indicator when looking at rocks in the field. Although agates occur in a variety of colors, any outstanding shades of red, orange, or brown should signal you to take a closer look.

Iron-oxide staining is found on nearly all agates to some degree, and generally covers much of the rock. Such staining can be many different colors, but the most common are shades of rust-red and yellow. Reddish oxidation of the mineral hematite is an indication of primary weathering and is usually displayed on exposed bands. Yellow-colored staining, called "limonite" develops on agates in two areas: within the pitted depressions on the extremely weathered exterior, or "husk", of the rock; and on the exposed banding surface, as intensified or secondary weathering of hematite. Sometimes these yellow areas are the only indication of a hidden prize. Many other rocks, however, exhibit similar yellow limonite staining, and you will need practice before you can easily differentiate these rocks from agates.

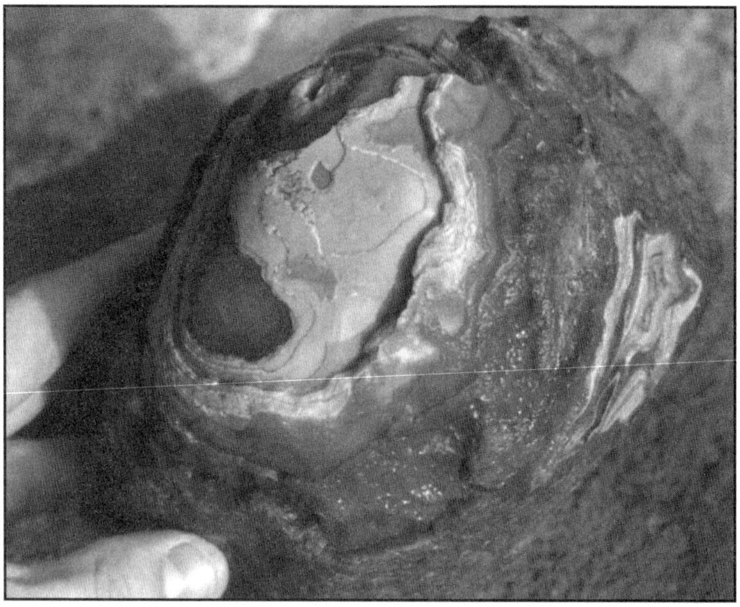

Intense pressure during glacial transport, together with abrasion from collisions in melt-water streams (and repeated freeze-thaw cycles), produced the unique feature in agates called "peeled texture". The peeled banding on this 9.04 pound specimen developed along inherently weak banding planes that "spalled" (broke off in layers) during glacial transport.

Translucence is an optical feature very useful in helping you spot dusty or dirty agates. Chalcedony quartz (the principal constituent of agates) allows light to penetrate it to some degree, producing a glow that distinguishes it from other rocks. Sunny days are best for observing translucence, and often this is the only clue to an agate's presence. Other quartz-rich rocks also display this optical effect, and the only way to confirm that a rock is an agate is to pick it up and take a closer look.

A **glossy, waxy appearance,** especially on a chipped or broken surface, is another clue the experienced eye will detect. Agate, like glass, has a curved or conchoidal fracture that is very often shiny. Such a surface can tip you off to the presence of an otherwise hidden agate.

Pitted texture is another very common feature of agates that you can look for while prospecting. The pits are actually the results of knobs or projections from an initial layer of softer mineral matter deposited on the wall of the cavity in which the agate formed. When the chalcedony that forms the agate was later deposited in the cavity, these projections left impressions on its exterior surface. Many other volcanic rocks also have this pitted appearance, due to the presence of small gas cavities called "vesicles" or the differential out-weathering of crystals. But with practice, you will be able to use these pits (sometimes called "pimples" or "pockmarks") successfully to distinguish agates from other rock types.

Iron oxide staining on the surfaces of agates is produced when tiny internal hematite particles oxidize when exposed to weathering by glacial abrasion. Several hematite particles rest upon gently undulating white to semitransparent banding, awaiting their day to provide coloration to the agate (15X).

Essay: The Big Agates

Size is probably the one aspect of the Lake Superior agate that inspires the most curiosity and discussion. While many people will often agree on the beauty and quality of a particular stone, such characteristics are, ultimately, a matter of opinion. Size, on the other hand, can be measured quantitatively. In terms of judging agates, size means weight. This is because the varying shapes of agates can be misleading: elongated and irregularly shaped stones appear heavier than they actually are, whereas more spherical stones are apt to seem smaller than their actual weight.

Experts differ on what they consider a "big" Lake Superior agate. In terms of rarity, any agate weighing more than one pound is "big"; the odds of finding an agate of this size are extremely low. You could hunt agates all your life and never find a high-quality stone weighing two pounds or more. This should not discourage beginning agate pickers, however, since the truly fine large agates seem to be most often found accidentally or by first-timers.

An inexperienced agate picker who happens upon a large stone, however, will sometimes impetuously smash or break it with a hammer to see what is on the inside. Stories of such errors by unknowing individuals are the ultimate horror for knowledgeable collectors. Not only are serious agate hunters disturbed by the thought of a rare large agate being smashed into little pieces, but they are also aware that large agates when cut open are usually a disappointment. Either the center or much of the rock is clear quartz or internal fractures scar what could have been a beautiful gemstone if left in its natural state.

People frequently ask, "What is the largest Lake Superior agate ever found?" This question is hard to answer for a couple of reasons. First, many large, but poor-quality agates, mostly composed of more than 75 percent clear quartz have been found but are not considered quality agates. Second, documenting a large agate by actually seeing and weighing it is sometimes very difficult. Stories are told of huge Lake Superior agates, some of them supposedly weighing between 200 and 300 pounds, but the existence of such stones is questionable at best. Long-time agate pickers probably rank with fisherman in their tendency to tell entertaining tall tales.

To my knowledge, the largest fortification Lake Superior agate of outstanding quality found in glacial drift, is the 21.62-pound specimen found by Ernest J. Counsell on his farm in New Haven, Iowa in 1958 (see portfolio, page C12). The next biggest nodule that I'm aware of is a 19.87-pound behemoth found by Nathan Horsch while picking rocks from a farm field near Isle, Minnesota, in 1988 when he was 14 years old. Nate's agate is mostly quartz, but it is still impressive and cut up with banding that snakes all through the stone and is what we call a "floater".

Another large Lake Superior agate that ranks near the top in size and quality is a 14.75-pound specimen found near Pine City, Minnesota, in 1925. This particular agate had an interesting history, in which I am proud to have played a part. It was discovered by a farmer plowing his fields who recognized it as an agate and kept it on his back porch as a doorstep. There the stone remained until 1935, when it was purchased for fifteen dollars by an agate collector named Audie Human. Mr. Human was the proud owner of the giant until his death in 1975. His widow then gave the agate to her husband's good friend LeRoy Peterson, an avid rock hound. Mr. Peterson, who carried the agate in a red-plaid bowling bag, displayed the stone at rock shows, gem shows, and county fairs for a decade. The agate was seen by thousands of admirers and became quite popular.

I purchased the agate from Mr. Peterson in January, 1986. You would think that in my hands it could rest for a while, but not so. Off it went again to a new home in Foley, Minnesota, this time to another Mr.

Peterson, who offered me four times the amount I had paid for it. As fate would have it, I got another opportunity and bought it backing 1991. It has stayed put for the last seventeen years and will continue to for the foreseeable future.

Recently, another giant was pulled from a gravel pit, ironically, from near the town of Isle, Minnesota, in October of 2007. Willie Thomson decided to hunt agates on a morning when he came up empty hunting for whitetail deer. He said he walked into the gravel pit, through a big puddle of water and up to a pile a large over-size rocks that had recently been moved. Sitting at the bottom along the edge of the pile was the 11.15-pound monster. My agate collector friend Bruce Peddle spotted the agate on Ebay and told me to check it out. That same evening Willie and I consummated a deal for the agate. I promised to tell his story in the next edition of my book and I'm happy to share it now.

While, many large and beautiful gemstones have already been found, enthusiasts cannot help but wonder what lies waiting to be discovered beneath the glacial overburden. Perhaps a 50-pound agate of unrivaled beauty is about to turn up in a farmer's field or fall from the wall of a gravel pit. Large agates are still out there to be discovered and the thrill of knowing that the next agate found could be a "big one" is what motivates the truly dedicated agate picker.

Essay: Grant's Agate

The following agate tale is one about sentiment and luck. As other diehard pickers know, finding a nice quality agate is hard enough, but to find a nice quality, *big* agate, is even harder. We have all traded stories about the many hours and miles it takes to find that big beauty. When that day comes and you do find that once-in-a-lifer, it's a day you'll never forget.

My day came May 12, 1990. Spring was in full bloom and the sun was shining bright. As usual on a Saturday morning I was up early and hitting my favorite colleting sites hard. On this particular Saturday, I had other thoughts on my mind besides agates. My wife Janet was nine months pregnant with our first baby and due any day. I had a pager on my belt and was waiting for it to go off at any moment. I knew sooner or later it would be show time.

I had been picking since 7:00 a.m. and although it was approaching noon, I decided to hit one more pile. As I pulled into the pit, I noticed that people were busy at work producing gravel. I decided not to stop and get in their way by picking agates, so I just drove around the sorted rock pile. As I drove slowly around the pile I noticed the dirtier, more recently dumped stones. Suddenly I saw it. It caught my eye instantly, with the characteristic waxy texture that made me slam on the brakes. I jumped out of my truck and grabbed the rock. It was an agate alright, and a big one too! I slowly turned the stone in my hands and rolled over a large finely-banded bulls-eye face. I started to shake with excitement, and began to look around to see if anyone was there to chase me away; or worse yet, take my agate and then chase me away. But no one was there; just pickers' paranoia. I wasn't going to top this find, so I hopped in my truck and headed for home.

As I headed down the road, I kept glancing over at the jewel I had just found. My initial guess was that it might be a five pounder. But as usual, the excitement made the rock look bigger. Before I got home I stopped at a deli for the official weigh-in: 3.50 pounds, by far my best big one.

It would be hard to believe that a guy could get so lucky twice in one week. Five days after I found the prize agate, Janet gave birth to an even bigger prize. A seven-pound eight ounce baby boy we named Grant.

Needless to say that special stone is called "Grant's Agate". It's even harder to believe that baby boy is now 6' 3" tall and will be beginning his freshman year in college next fall (2008) at my Alma matter-the University of Minnesota-Duluth. Even though our son Grant will soon be leaving the nest, his agate will be safe at home.

It's hard to believe that eighteen years have gone by since I found the 3.50-pounder I call "Grant's Agate" on May 12, 1990. My son Grant was born five days later and will be heading off to college this fall at my alma mater, the University of Minnesota-Duluth.

Essay: Remember Me?

The first part of this next story was told in my most recent book, *"The Lake Superior Agate: One Man's Journey,"* published in 2001. I'll give you a quick recap, and then I'll tell the rest of the story. I wrote a chapter about the annual Moose Lake Agate Days gem show, held the third weekend in July in Moose Lake, Minnesota. I always have a booth where I sell agate books, puzzles, posters, prints, and, of course, rough and polished specimens. At the 1998 show, during the height of the frenzy, around noon on Saturday, a young boy walked up to my table with a large agate in his hands. I immediately zoned in on the stone and asked if I could take a look at it. He handed me the stone that was bright white and red in color and felt like it weighed about 3 pounds.

A crowd of people began to form as I went into my salesman mode. *"So young man; is the agate for sale?"* I said. He looked at me, then up at his father, turned back to me, and shrugged his shoulders. Realizing I had a tough customer, I pulled out the heavy artillery and said, *"What if I gave you enough money to buy a new bicycle?"* Once again, he looked up at his dad, then back at me, and this time shook his head from side to side. *"Tough negotiator,"* I thought. Not to be denied, I tried again, *"How about if I give you enough money to buy two bikes?"* The young boy went through the same routine and shut me down, as the crowd of people laughed in unison.

Realizing I'd met my match, I asked if I could take a couple photographs, which he allowed me to do. I then turned to get a pen and a piece of paper to get his phone number and, when I turned back, he, his father, and the agate were gone.

By the time I was ready to publish *"Journey,"* I hadn't forgotten the young boy and his agate. I decided to tell the story, and included a picture of him holding the rock. In the caption, I asked for another chance, and included my phone number. It was a long shot, but even though I knew I'd probably never hear from him again, it was an entertaining story.

Five years later, in May of 2003, I retrieved my mail from my P.O. Box in Minneapolis. Amongst the usual pile of letters and advertising was a letter with no return address. Curious, I opened the letter and pulled out a picture. I instantly recognized the face of the teenage boy holding a familiar rock in front of a blooming crabapple tree. It was him! He had obviously seen the book and, instead of calling, had sent me a photograph of himself in the same pose with the agate that I'd put in my book. I laughed out loud when I turned the picture over, and there was a Post-it note with two words scribbled on the back: *"Remember me?"*

The picture got me excited thinking that "mystery boy" might be coming to Moose Lake in a couple of months and I'd have a chance to buy the agate. In preparation of his return, I posted both pictures of him outside my booth, with the words written below his pictures, *"Have you seen me?"* Unfortunately, at the end of the day on Sunday, "mystery boy" was a no-show.

Fifteen months later, at the gem and mineral show in Cottage Grove, Minnesota, in October of 2004, I gave a lecture about Lake Superior agates. After my talk, several people came up to me to ask questions and look at the specimens I'd brought to display. As I answered questions, a face with an impish smile appeared within the group. I pointed to the teenage boy surrounded by members of his smiling family and said, *"It's you! What is your name?"* True to form, he looked at me and said, *"Jon."* Everybody laughed, and then they explained how his older sister found his picture in the book. He said they decided to play a joke by sending me the picture. I told him his joke worked quite well, and how I missed him at Moose Lake. I also told him I was still interested in his agate. Jon was now fifteen years old and, semi-jokingly, I said, *"I suppose you'll want enough money to buy a car now?"* Before leaving, he said he'd call me if he decided to sell the agate.

By the spring of 2006, I'd all but given up on ever buying the agate. Then, one day, I received an email that simply read, *"I think I'm ready to sell."* I knew right away that it was Jon, and we made plans to get-together. On June 17, 2006, on a hot, muggy day, Janet, Grant, and Amanda, and I all piled into the car and drove to the Morell family farm near St. Cloud, Minnesota. They invited us in for lemonade, and we laughed about the humorous drama of the last eight years. At one point, Jon turned to me said, *"I'm not going to torture you anymore; I'm ready to sell the agate."* He said he did want to buy a car, and we agreed on a price that would allow him to make a sizable down payment.

Before leaving, we took a few more pictures, including one with Jon holding his agate in the now-famous pose under the same crabapple tree. Jon's agate now resides in my collection and is one of the nicest "floaters" I've ever seen. One thing of which Jon can rest assured is that I will always *remember him!*

Jon Morell was probably the toughest negotiator I ever met. He made me wait eight years before he sold me his agate. I took the first picture of Jon in 1998; he sent me the second picture in 2003, and I took the third picture of him the day he sold me the agate on June 17, 2006.

CHAPTER 3
This is NOT a Lake Superior Agate

Why I never wrote about this before, I don't know. It is long past time that I helped people understand not only what agates look like, but what rocks are NOT Lake Superior agates. In the early days of my collecting, I went off on more than one wild goose chase for an agate that turned out to be chert, jasper, or some other variety of quartz-rich rock. I still get many calls from people who think they've found a monster Laker.

I once had an attorney write to me, insisting he knew the whereabouts of the biggest Lake Superior agate in the world. He said it was over four feet across, had excellent banding, and estimated its weight at several tons. When we met for lunch and he showed me the pictures, I regretfully informed him that his record agate was actually a silicified limestone. Although it was a very pretty rock, it was not going to yield the big payday he was hoping for.

It is easy for inexperienced collectors to make this mistake, since the dominant composition of many other rocks besides Lakers is fine-grained quartz. The physical properties of many varieties of quartz-rich rocks are very similar to agate, such as a waxy luster and glassy appearance. The majority of rocks commonly mistaken for Lake Superior agate generally fall into the following categories:

Iron Formation – People commonly mistake "BIF"– or "banded iron formation"– as agate due to the often well-developed alternating, red-and-gray colored banding. Banded iron formation is relatively common in Superior lobe glacial deposits, but it doesn't have the overall translucent appearance of agate. Sometimes specimens will have translucent chert layers between the red iron-rich bands. Even though they are not true Lakers, they can be quite beautiful and still worth carrying home.

Jasper – This rock type is composed of nearly 100% crypto-crystalline quartz, but does not have the characteristic banding of agate and generally forms in massive deposits, as opposed to vesicle-filling of volcanic rocks. Jasper can be brightly-colored and pretty, and some pieces can still be used for lapidary.

Chert – This rock is a very common variety of crypto-crystalline quartz that usually occurs as a secondary replacement within sedimentary rocks. Color varies from colorless to white and yellow, with some specimens exhibiting bright reds and oranges. Chert can also exhibit poorly defined banding, which is a tip-off of an agate impersonator.

Silicified Limestone – This rock type is very common and often has a similar appearance to chert. Silicified limestone will often retain structures of the original material secondary quartz has replaced, such as bedding, which is often confused with agate banding, and fossils, such as coral. Sometimes, limestone cavities are replaced with areas of banded agate that is usually white or colorless. These areas are often associated with irregular-shaped, tiny quartz crystal-lined open cavities called vug pockets. Even though they are not Lakers, some silicified limestone specimens can be quite beautiful.

Petrified Wood – Many people don't realize how common petrified wood is in glacial deposits. Pieces normally have dull white, yellow, and brown colors and usually retain the evenly-spaced annual rings that are often mistaken for agate banding.

"Leaverite" – Although the term has been jokingly used by rock-hounds for decades to mean *"Leave 'er right there,"* it is essentially what collectors should probably do with most material they pick up early on in their collecting careers. However, with a little persistence, it doesn't take long for a collector's eye to figure out what is agate and what is not!

To see examples of these non-agate types in color turn to portfolio page C-13.

CHAPTER 4
How an Agate is Formed

Not only is Lake Superior agate remarkably beautiful, but its formation comprises a unique series of events approached by no other gemstone. The history of the Lake Superior agate spans a time period so lengthy that it makes the time required for a mountain range to form and erode away seem insignificant by comparison.

The formation of the Lake Superior agate began between 1.1 and 1.2 billion years ago, during the late Precambrian Era. At that time, the continental crust that would become the heartland of North America began to split apart in what is called a "rifting event." The rift resulted from internal forces that tended to stretch the earth's crust, breaking it into two pieces.

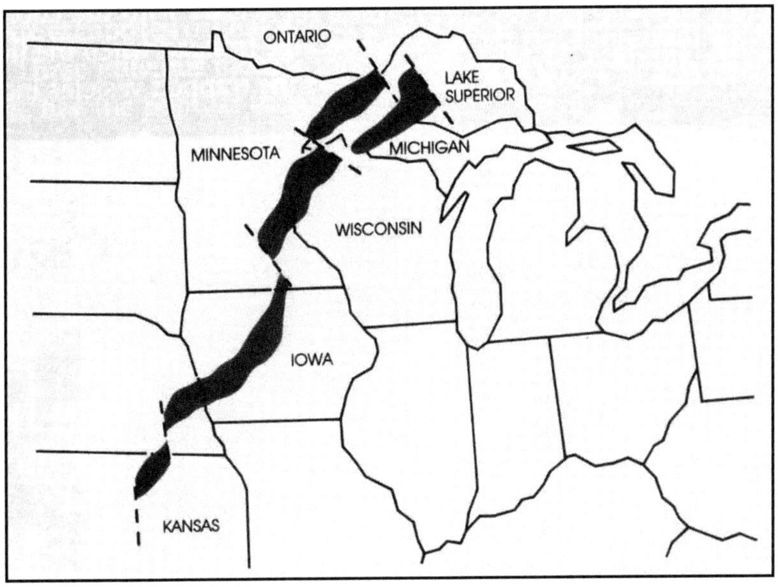

Figure 4-1: The dark areas show the extent of the Precambrian Age (1.1 to 1.2 billion years ago) rifting event that preceded the formation of Lake Superior agates. Remnant lava flows are still exposed along the North Shore of Lake Superior and in places along the St. Croix River Valley. (Redrawn from *Minnesota's Geology*, Ojakangas and Matsch).

This awesome event was accomplished by the upwelling of hot, molten rock material called "magma" from deep within the earth. When the magma reached the surface, it poured out as lava flows that cooled to form new rock that filled the newly created rift basin. In North America, the rift extended from what is now eastern Lake Superior, southwestward into what is now Kansas.

Before this rifting event could tear North America into two continents separated by a new ocean basin, the process stopped. The lava poured out as flows that piled up one on top of another. Hundreds of these flows eventually accumulated into a pile close to 22,000 feet (over four miles) in total thickness and spread out over thousands of square miles. You can imagine what four miles of lava flows would weigh!

Indeed, this sudden accumulation of billions of tons of rock actually pressed down on the crust of the earth to form a depression or trough (Figure 4-2). Part of this trough is now occupied by Lake Superior. Not only did this low spot help produce the beautiful lake, but it also played an important role in the distribution of the Lake Superior agate.

The next phase in the development of the semi-precious gemstone took place within the individual lava flows. As each flow poured out onto the surface, escaping the heat and pressure with the earth, it began to cool. As the lava cooled and solidified, it gave off steam (H_2O) and carbon dioxide (CO_2). Gas-filled cavities in the form of bubbles, or "vesicles", rose toward the top of the individual flows, allowing the gases to escape as the vesicles reached the lava surface. The vesicles grew in size as they moved upward through the flow in response to the decreasing pressure in the surrounding lava (think of the gas bubbles of carbon dioxide that rise to a head of foam in a glass of beer as it is poured, or the air bubbles from a scuba diver's exhaled breath that rise from the depths and grow in size until they reach the surface).

Within each lava flow, the rising vesicles raced for release with the cooling of the ever-stiffening flow. Many thousands lost the race and became trapped when the flow hardened. A side view or cross-section of a lava flow clearly shows the trapped vesicles increasing in both number and size toward the top of the flow. Within these vesicles, the Lake Superior agate formed.

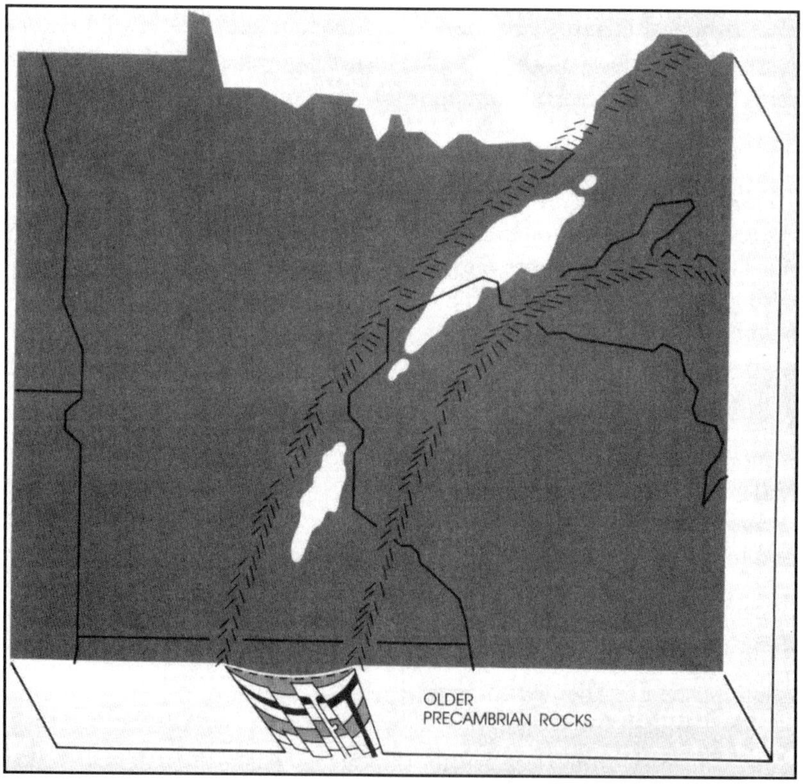

Figure 4-2: This diagram shows how the Lake Superior region may have appeared after the rifting event ceased. The topographic basin was created by the weight of the extruded lava flows pressing down on the crust of the earth, together with the collapse of the vacated magma chamber at depth. (Redrawn form *Minnesota's Geology*, Ojakangas and Matsch).

During the lava flows final cooling and solidification by crystallization into rock, contraction took place, producing an inter-connecting network of cracks called "fractures." These fractures produced a network connecting the vesicles throughout the entire flow. The intensity of fracturing is typically greatest at the top of a flow, due in part to the increased number of vesicle there. Fracturing at and near the surface is further enhanced by weathering, especially frost action. This highly permeable network of vesicles and fractures played an important part in the formation of agates.

The next event in the formation of the Lake Superior agate took place well after the host lava flows were deposited. The time between the depositing or "deposition" of individual lava flows is speculative; using current volcanic activity as a guide, it could have been a matter of hours or hundreds of years. During the igneous activity that resulted in the deposition of these flows, "magmatic" waters, (water associated with volcanism), were generated. In addition to these "juvenile" waters, other water trapped for millions of years below the surface (connate water), together with percolating rainwater and melted snow (meteoric water), were mixed and heated at depth.

These waters carried silica (SiO_2) and other dissolved minerals through the fracture systems into the vesicles of deeper, earlier flows. Although more then 99 percent of Lake Superior agates are composed of chalcedony quartz many other minerals also crystallized from these solutions. These minerals include iron, calcite, epidote, prehnite, chlorite, and various radiating zeolites, like the popular thomsonite.

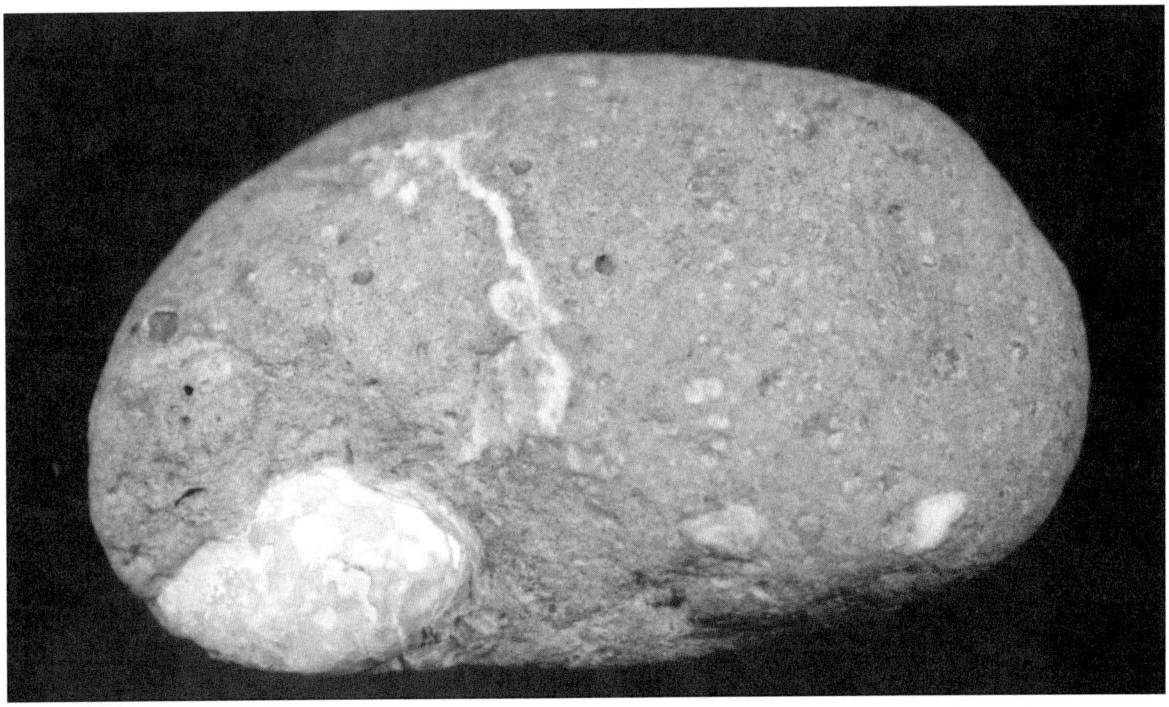

An agate amydule, at lower left, is still enclosed in the host basalt cobble. Notice the quartz-filled fracture circling away from the amygdule that solutions followed into and out of the vesicle.

During the "wet" phase, the formation of the agate began. Debate continues over the exact conditions at the time of formation, including the chemical composition of the solutions, temperature, and pressure. These conditions and their fluctuations produced the various types and particular features of agates.

As the silica-rich solutions flowed through the fractures and vesicles, they precipitated a thin layer or band of very fine-grained quartz called "chalcedony," which lined the entire vesicle wall. As later solutions entered and exited, band after band of chalcedony was deposited, until eventually the vesicle was completely filled. These mineral-filled vesicles are called "amygdules." The successive bands of chalcedony were probably caused by "pulses" of solutions passing through the entire volcanic pile in a circular, convection-current type of movement. Here again, the time between each pulse of solution and the subsequent deposition of each layer of chalcedony is uncertain; it may have been as little as a few seconds.

Many people believe the activity within the vesicles during chalcedony deposition was similar to coffee-pot percolator action. This percolator action could explain the similar banding sequences seen in many agates. Band thickness and groupings are surely related to the differing percolation periods, temperature, and pressure conditions, as well as the solution composition.

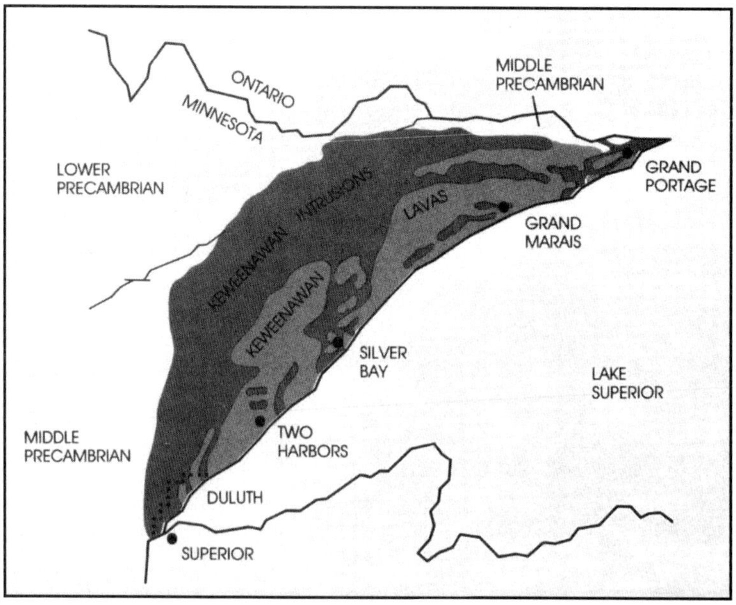

Figure 4-3: The North Shore Volcanic Group as it is presently mapped along Lake Superior (Redrawn from *Minnesota's Geology*, Ojankangas and Matsch).

When the rifting of North America stopped, a long quiet period of erosion began that started to disintegrate the thick pile of lava flows called the North Shore Volcanic Group (Figure 4-3). The lava flows, composed mainly of minerals other than quartz, began to break down chemically and physically. Quartz is a very stable mineral that will not break down readily even when exposed to the atmosphere and its destructive elements. Chemical weathering and the physical breakdown of the upper lava flows resulted in the removal of the lava matrix and exposure of the quartz agates and larger rocks. Perhaps millions of years ago the surface of the old rift zone was littered with agates with no one to claim them.

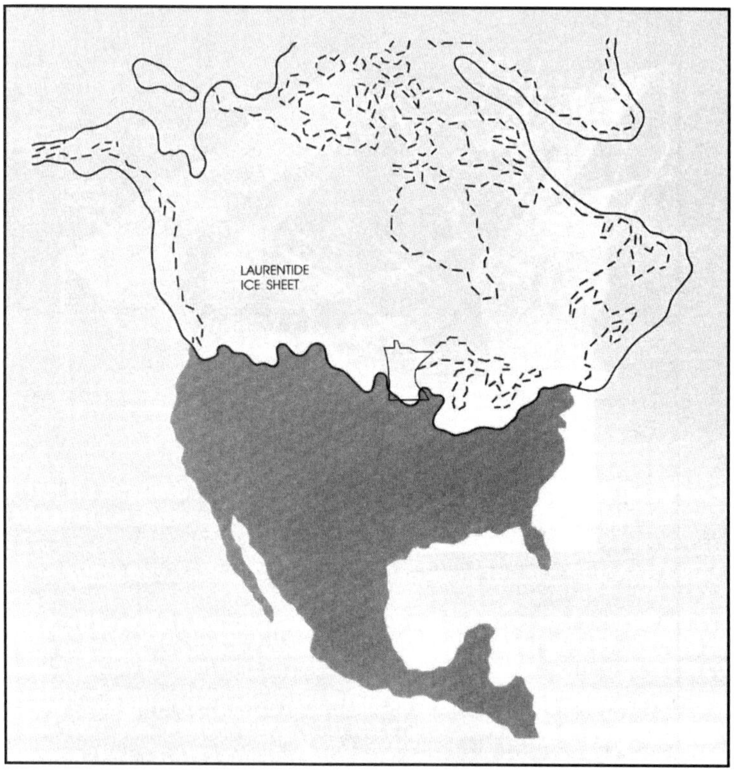

Figure 4-4: The extent of the Laurentide Ice Sheet in North America roughly 16,000 years ago, during the latter part of the Wisconsin Glaciation (Redrawn for *North America and the Great Ice Age*, Matsch).

The final chapter in the history of the Lake Superior agate took place a relatively short time ago (in geological time, that is!) during the Quaternary Period; better known as the Great Ice Age. Beginning about 2 million years ago the earth underwent a series of dramatic climatic changes, including long periods of cool temperatures worldwide. During these cool periods, continental ice sheets developed in both the northern and southern hemispheres, and began to inch their way toward the equator. At least four distinct glaciations occurred during the Quaternary period, the first three being the Nebraskan, the Kansan and the Illinoian. The ice of the fourth and most recent glacial period, the Wisconsin, began melting about 14,000 years ago and is responsible for the present topographic features we see today in much of northern North America.

During the Wisconsin glaciation, all of Canada, most of Alaska, and much of the northern half of the United States was covered with ice. The massive body of ice, called the Laurentide ice sheet, was more than a mile thick at its center, which was located over what is now Hudson Bay (Figure 4-4). Along the margin of the ice sheet, protruding tongues or "lobes" of ice followed topographic low areas, flowing very much like thick pancake batter. One of these lobes, the mile-thick Superior lobe, advanced southward along the Lake Superior trough approximately 75,000 year ago. Roughly 30,000 years ago, the Superior lobe entered Minnesota, and 16,000 years ago it stalled at its maximum extent, covering areas west and south of the Twin Cities (Figure 4-5).

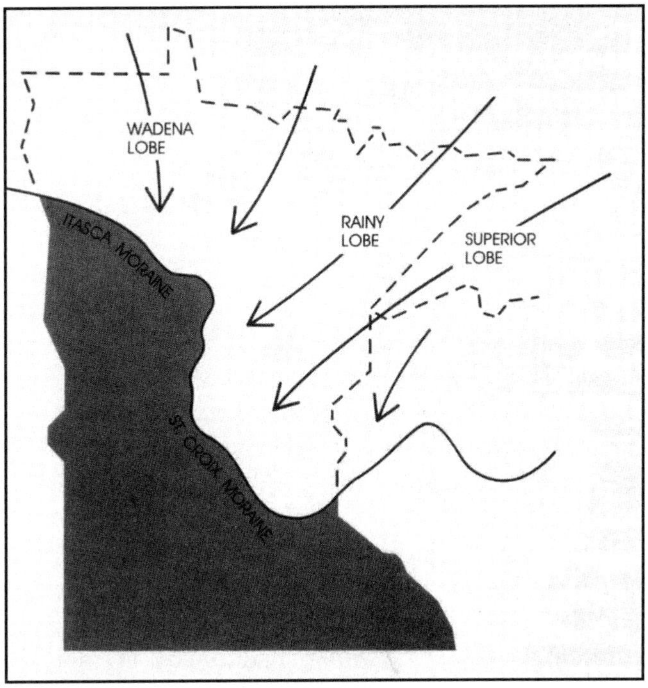

Figure 4-5: Only the Superior lobe carried agate into Minnesota because it followed the Superior trough which contains the agate-bearing lavas (Redrawn from *Minnesota's Geology*, Ojakangas and Matsch).

During the Superior lobe's trek southward, the agate-filled lava flows and the eroded-out agates lying on the surface were in the direct path of the encroaching ice. The glacier picked up agates littering the surface and carried them along on the trip south. The crushing action and cycle of freezing and thawing at the base of the glacier also freed many agates from within the depths of the lava flows and transported them as well. As the glacier advanced, moving plastically, the glacier's internal motions acted like a huge rock tumbler, abrading, fracturing and "rough polishing" the agates. Such abrasion "opens" the stones and exposes their internal beauty.

When the glaciers reached their maximum extent, the Superior lobe had spread agates and other debris throughout the northeastern and central areas of Minnesota and extreme northwestern Wisconsin. Then the global climate changed, and a period of warmth triggered melting and the retreat of the Superior lobe. Abrasion of the agates, however, was not yet complete.

Along the margins of the glacier were ridges of ice-transported material, called "moraines." Cutting into these moraines were rivers and streams swollen with waters from melting glacial ice. The streams carried sand and gravel, including agates, and deposited these sediments as "outwash." These streams performed the final abrasion and rough polishing of the agates (Figure 4-6).

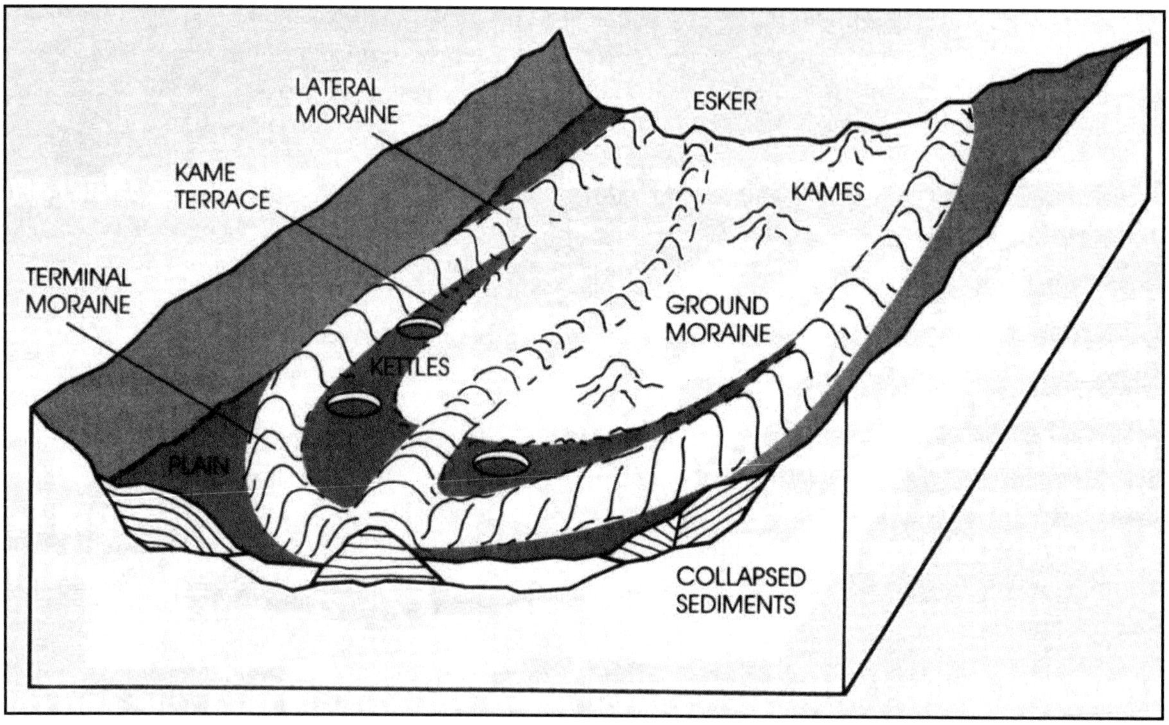

Figure 4-6: This is a simplified diagram of depositional features associated wit the advance and retreat of a glacier. Moraines are deposited directly by the ice and outwash by melt-water.

The majority of agates came to rest in moraine and outwash deposits. The agates trapped within and beneath the glacier, farther "up-ice" from the moraine deposits, eventually melted out and were scattered more sparsely. Subsequent re-advances of the Superior lobe in response to minor climatic fluctuations deposited recessional moraines and more agates in areas around Duluth. As the ice receded into Canada, the melt-water filled the original basin or trough it had followed into Minnesota, forming an earlier predecessor to Lake Superior, called Glacial Lake Duluth.

The final touch of individuality that distinguishes the Lake Superior agate from other agates occurred after glacial erosion and deposition. A noted earlier, although silica comprised the major part of the dissolved material in the warm solutions, other chemicals were present in trace amounts and were precipitated along with the chalcedony. One important minor constituent was ferrous iron (Fe^{++}). Abrasion during glacial transport exposed the iron within agates, and after deposition by the glaciers, the iron reacted with oxygen from the atmosphere to produce a natural rust as a stain. The concentration of iron and the amount of oxidation determines the color, ranging from red to brown, within or between an agate's bands.

As you can see, the formation of the Lake Superior agate was a long and complex process. By it is this unusual history that has given the agate its vivid spectrum of color and unrivaled beauty.

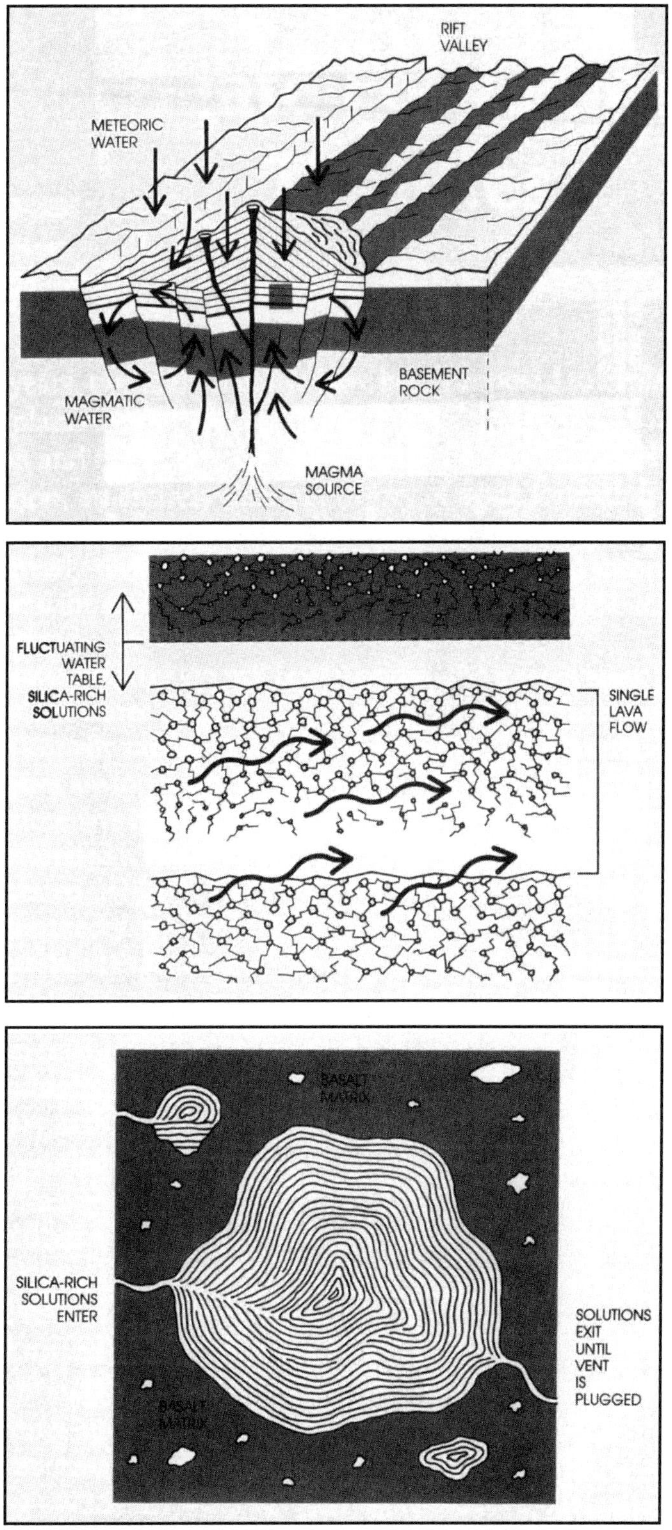

Figure 4-7: The diagrams at right, each an enlargement of the small square in the preceding diagram, illustrate the formation of Lake Superior agates.

Beginning 1.1 to 1.2 billion years ago, tensional forces deep within the earth caused a huge crack to open in the earth's crust. Magma welled up from the mantle producing faulting, earthquakes and volcanic eruptions with the deposition of thousands of lava flows at the surface (Diagram #1). As the lava flows were extruded and began to cool, carbon dioxide (CO_2) gas and water vapor (H_2O) were given off. Within each flow, pockets of gas called vesicles, rose and grew in size until they escaped out the top or became trapped as the flow hardened. Further cooling and contraction produced cracks between vesicles that continued throughout the flow.

Meteoric water from rain and melted snow percolated down through the lava pile and mixed with hot magmatic water at depth. These hot waters leached mineral matter (silicon dioxide or quartz) along with minor accessory minerals (iron oxides) from basement rocks producing silica-rich solutions (Diagram #2). These solutions circulated within the rift valley system in circular convection cell patterns driven by high heat flow from the deep-seated magma chamber.

Within the porous system of vesicles and fractures, the water table rose and fell with the solution supply. The system fluctuated in response to the pulsating heat flow associated with the cyclic volcanism. During periods of high silica solution water table levels, individual fractures and vesicles became flooded. When the water table level fell, many vesicles drained of solutions leaving a thin band of chalcedony that crystallized on the inside of the vesicle (Diagram #3). Subsequent fluctuations of the silica-rich solution supply deposited band after band of chalcedony as agate.

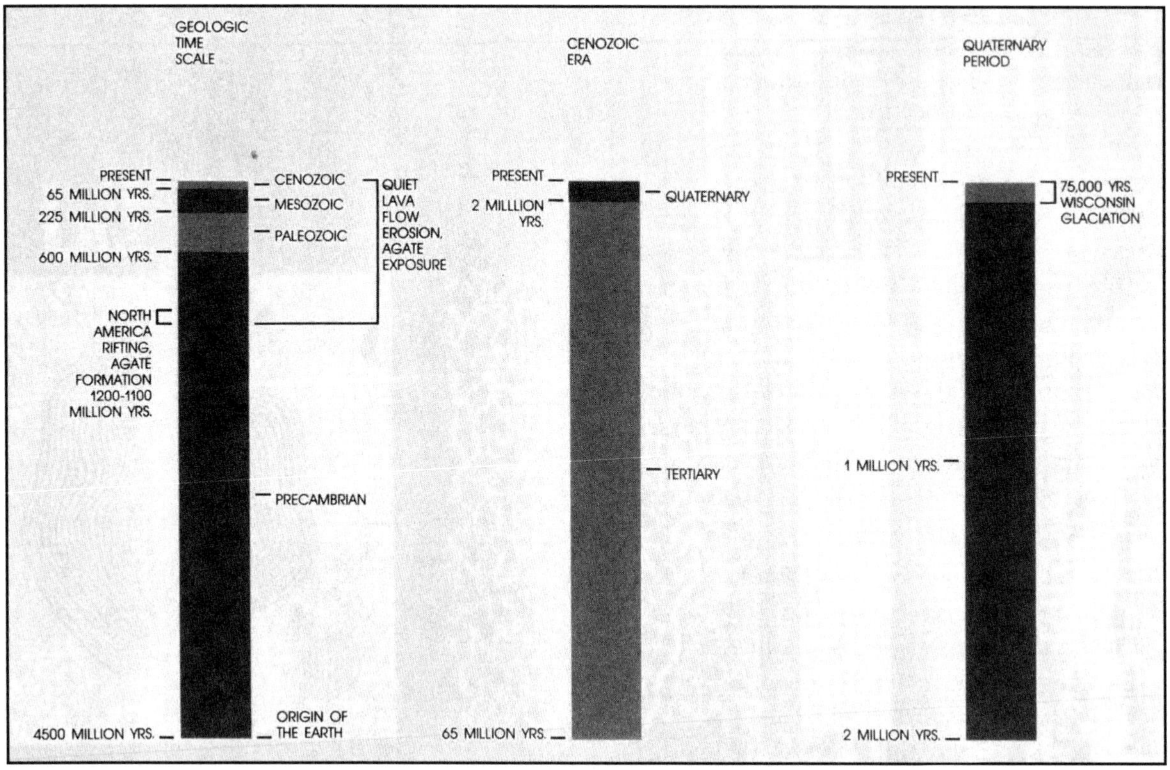

Figure 4-8: Geologic Time Scale

Discussion: Agate Formation Theories

In the last 200 years, two main theories have been proposed to explain the formation of agates. Each theory explains a different view of filling vesicles in cooled lava. One involves successive band deposition and the other involves a single nodule of silica gel which then separates into bands. In addition, an entirely different theory of agate formation was recently proposed by Benjamin M. Shaub (1989). Much like arguments over religion and politics, the prevailing wisdom is greatly divided. Currently, none of the proposed theories adequately explains all agate types and the myriad of internal structures. It seems that the answer is more complex than anyone imagined.

The following discussion will briefly explain the present agate formation theories, as well as important structures in agates that surely hold the clues to agate formation.

First, let's briefly explain the basics of each theory. The one thing everybody does agree on is that Lake Superior agates are formed in association with volcanic rocks. Things begin to diverge at this point. The successive band theory states that agates are formed by multiple flooding of vesicles with silica-saturated solution. Each filling of the vesicles leaves a layer or band of chalcedony, which is repeated until the cavity is partially or completely filled. Chapter Three explains my version of this theory.

A closely related explanation for agate formation also involves secondary silica-rich solution entering a vesicle. However, in this case once the vesicle is filled with the solution, it does not drain away. The cavity remains filled and banding is formed by differential separation of silica into hydrous and anhydrous layers from a single gelatinous solution. This theory holds that after the gel has segregated into bands, the bands are then deformed plastically by internal and/or external forces producing various structures.

The newest theory by Shaub (1989) proposes that agates were formed when the host magma was still hot and fluid. Mr. Shaub suggests that "colloidal silica is released from high silica magma and agglutinates into a mass swimming in the magma that forms into spheres by surface tension" (Shaub, page 24). The banding and other internal structures then form from the gelatinous masses "according to the geophysical and geochemical laws" (Shaub, page 24). "At some time the dense mass of colloidal silica will solidify into the remarkable concentric banded structure of the eye-catching colorful banded agates" (Shaub, pages 25-26). The banding mechanism quoted here is assumed to be similar to the theory of differential separation of silica presented by R. E. Liesgang (1915), Dr. H.G. McPerson (1989) and others.

The three theories differ greatly, with each presenting a scenario that begs to be further explored. A better understanding of the conditions that were present during agate formation can be gained by close examination of several physical structures. We have all observed many of these structures. If one has not, a better appreciation of these precious stones can be enjoyed if you take a closer look.

Part of the problem in understanding these features is confusion caused by viewing internal structures in two dimensions. Interpretation of structures must be performed while always remembering that they occur in three dimensions. This is, of course, very difficult because we don't have x-ray vision. Lake Superior agates are especially tough because most specimens are covered with secondary oxidation products, mainly iron oxide and limonite. This makes viewing structures beneath the glossy surface difficult to impossible. Cut and polished specimens offer the best view of internal structures and significantly reduce the oxidation product problem so prevalent along the exterior surface of glacially weathered agates (this is not an endorsement for cutting and polishing Lake Superior agates).

Entrance Channels and Escape Tubes

This common structure occurs as an obvious disruption in the continuity of the banding pattern. To supporters of the single silica gel theory, the deformed bands represent escape tubes. The banding has been plastically deformed by gel mass moving from the interior toward the exterior. In this case, the moving gel is extruded by expansion from heat generated by chemical reactions which occur during crystallization. The amount of heat needed to produce such movement is unclear but it would have to be small. It is believed that a relatively small amount of heat would be generated during crystallization, even in larger agates.

Close-up view of exit channels showing telescoping nature of curved bands that crystallized as solutions were leaving the vesicle (15X).

In Shaub's model, "parts of the agate bands have been pushed outward toward the periphery of the nodule. The pressure that created the bulges was derived from contraction of the surrounding rhyolite during cooling" (Shaub, page 25). Keep in mind that the silica nodule was already formed in the hot magma. If contraction of the stiffening surrounding lava produced pressure around the still plastic nodule, it seems that the bulges would be along the exterior of the nodule. Shrinking lava might be expected to crack in a radial pattern away from the nodule. The surrounding pressure would force the still plastic agate into the cracks like jello being forced between fingers when squeezed. The movement of material outward but within the confines of the nodule is more difficult to visualize using this model.

The successive-band theory explains these structures as the channels that silica-rich solutions followed into and out of the vesicle. The pinching of the band into the duct, which looks similar to plastic deformation, is actually a flow structure. The vesicle was initially filled with silica-rich solution under pressure. While flooded, a layer of chalcedony then begins to crystallize and adhere to the cavity wall or previously crystallized band. The individual characteristics of the band are dependent upon the composition of the solution and length of time in the vesicle. When the pressure gradient drops, the remaining solution is then pulled out. The relatively high velocity of exiting solution, under negative pressure, would allow less cryptocrystalline chalcedony to crystallize upon final approach and entrance into the escape channel as the solution is sucked out. This flow velocity of solution idea would also apply to the pinching and swelling of individual band thickness within the agate not associated with entrance/exit channels. This model conjures up an active cavity within the lava flow with solutions moving into, through, and out like blood through a living creature. The "heart" driving these flowing solutions is the fluctuating heat and pressure associated with the active volcanism which produced the lava.

I can't help but see these structures as escape channels. It seems to me that when closely examining specimens, I can almost always find the main entrance channel that solutions followed into and out of the agate. Often, the main of solution activity can be traced by visualizing the banding pattern in three dimensions. As can be seen, the origin of entrance/escape channels can be interpreted differently depending on how one views how an agate is formed.

Similar Banding Sequences

Another structure easily recognized upon close examination of Lake Superior agates is "similar banding sequences" (See Portfolio, page 73). Nearly every specimen of fortification agate will contain, wholly or in part, nearly identify, repeating sets of similar bands. The sequences are comprised of some repetitive combination of banding color, texture, iron-oxide content, and other accessory minerals. One example is the classic "red and white" agate. Upon close examination, each red and white banding set is quite complex. A typical set might include a white band, a clear band and a red band.

The white band is usually comprised of fibrous chalcedony needles aligned perpendicular to the banding plane. The adjacent zone is relatively clear or transparent. It is within this area, under magnification, that copper and sulfide minerals commonly occur. Where present, these minerals are aligned perpendicular to the banding similar to the white chalcedony needles. The clear zone is commonly the same thickness as the white zone. Last is an iron-oxide rich red or orange layer that is usually quite thin relative to the clear and white layers. This layer, in many ways, is the most interesting. The bulk of the iron-oxide producing the red color commonly occurs as disseminated particles. In some specimens, "oxidation halos" surrounding the particle can be seen. These "halos" and iron oxide dendrites occur within this layer parallel to the banding plane.

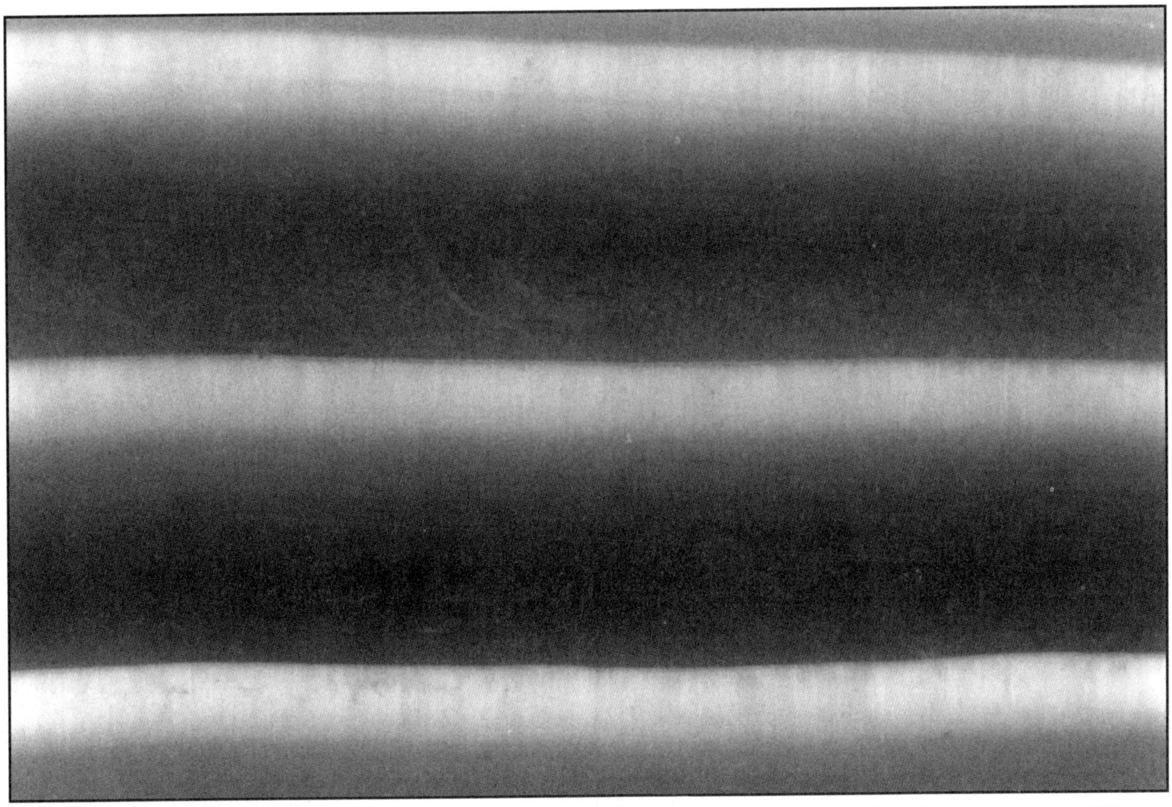

Two and a half sets of a similar banding sequence typically found in a banded red and white agate (30X).

These complex banding sequences occur with amazing frequency and consistency of structure. Whether from a single gelatinous mass or from rhythmic deposition of silica solutions, similar banding sequence formation is probably the same. One idea is that segregation of material within the solution occurs by ionic lineation. In this model, the fibrous chalcedony aligns itself at the base of the sequence with the iron-oxide material being ionically repelled to the opposite side of the layer. Sandwiched in between is the clear, transparent zone with suspended copper, and other minerals, floating perpendicularly aligned to the banding plane. The copper is typically seen as an elongate aggregate mass that is frozen into position as if being pulled at each end by magnetic forces. Whatever the force that separates and aligns material, it produces separate zones or layers.

Most agates exhibit similar banding sequences for at least part of the specimen. But banding characteristics can change dramatically, seemingly, without rhyme or reason. In many specimens, crystalline quartz layers alternate with clear, white, and/or red chalcedony. We call this type of agate a "floater". Sometimes the beautiful banding formation process ceases altogether with the remaining interior volume of the agate made of quartz crystals. These agates are the scourge of most collectors. These sudden changes in banding characteristics may represent abrupt changes in temperature, pressure and solution composition. The successive band deposition theory works well to explain these internal agate structures.

Each pulse of the solution fills the vesicle with same fluid or gel composition which then aligns into zones during crystallization. The number of banding sets within the sequence depends on the number of pulses of solution of similar composition pumped into the vesicle. If at some point during agate formation the solution or gel composition changes, then the banding sequence will change. "Quartzballs", or agates comprised almost entirely of crystal quartz, and "floaters" can be explained well using this theory. Floaters, with alternating chalcedony bands and crystalline quartz layers, also appear in similar banding sequences. For crystalline quartz to form, the temperature and /or pressure conditions must be different. In addition, the composition of the solution is different, with significantly less iron-oxide and other dissolved/secondary minerals.

Crystal Impressions

Crystal impressions are commonly observed on the husk of agates and are particularly interesting. Their origin is relatively simple. Minerals of composition other than quartz crystallized inside the vesicle before successive silica solutions or single gel were deposited. Both models can easily explain their occurrence.

Shaub's theory explains crystal impressions in a much different way. The colloidal silica nodule suspended in the molten magma falls to the bottom of the magma chamber like molten wax in "lava lamps". At the bottom of the chamber, previously crystallized minerals are present. "The soft gelatinous colloidal silica sphere when spread out over the rough mass becomes indented by the crystals (irregular objects) on the floor" (Shaub, pages 34-35). There are two problems with this scenario. If the nodule rests on the chamber floor, then there should not be crystal impressions on other parts of the agate than the flat bottom. Crystal impressions occur on all sides of many agates. Lake Superior agates are renowned for frequent well developed crystal impressions. The second problem is that the crystal imprints commonly observed on agates have shapes showing that they were produced by minerals that would not occur in molten magma. These minerals include calcite, pyrite, barite and others. These minerals are common secondary minerals observed in vesicles of exposed lavas. Unfortunately natural weathering and glacial transport of Lake Superior agates has long since dissolved away the impression-forming minerals.

Water-Level Banding

One of the most common types of Lake Superior agate is the one that could yield the most information. The perfectly straight banding so often seen in lakers appears to have a relatively simple explanation for its formation.

The parallel banding always develops at what was the bottom of the vesicle and accumulates upward in what appears to be obvious sequential deposition. I think all agate theorists agree that the parallel banding is a gravity induced structure. The problem with water-levels agates is that the single-gel camp has great difficulty in effectively explaining their formation. One idea is that SiO_2 particles precipitating from a fluid coagulate into horizontal bands (Landmesser, "The Problem of Agate Genesis," page 118). Other single-gel ideas suggest a similar "raining-out" of silica to accumulate at the bottom of the vesicle.

This explanation is rather simplistic and does not even begin to explain the complex microstructures within horizontal bands, let alone the multiple layers that continue up and around the vesicle wall. To accumulate the silica within each horizontal layer takes some designated period of time. This event must then stop before the next period of accumulation begins. This clearly represents a multiple deposition sequence.

This banding pattern in this $^1/_2$-pound Lake Superior water-level agate suggests that successive waves of silica-rich solutions filled the cavity first and then lost fluid pressure allowing the bulk of the solution to settle at the bottom.

Further evidence that water-level structure is produced by multiple events can be found in manmade rock-concrete. A common, and very destructive, event that occurs in concrete structures exposed to moisture is alkali-silica reaction (ASR). This moisture driven reaction occurs when unstable siliceous aggregate (quartzite, shale, chert, rhyolite, etc.) combine with sodium and potassium alkalies within the high pH (>11) environment of concrete. The result is a volumetric expansion of the concrete with the production of a silica-gel. Numerous cracks form from the expansion with the silica-gel migrating into the cracks and open air voids. Sound familiar?

Close examination of these deposits show obvious layering which is representative of separate ASR events in response to repeated exposure to moisture. ASR deterioration in concrete is progressive, occurring slowly over many years. This appears to be an accidental manmade analog to agate formation. Roger Pabian proposes that alkaline water (pH above 9) is essential to leach silica into solution, mobilize and form agates (Banded Agate: Origins and Inclusions, June 1994). This is virtually identical to what happens in concrete.

As you can see, the debate is exhaustive but interesting. None of the current theories can explain all agate types and individual structures. Obviously, agate formation is more complex than many thought. Perhaps we need to consider aspects of each theory. The secret to agate formation will eventually be unraveled when the internal structures are understood. This work must be performed without bias to a particular theory. Only then will the correct answers be learned. For now, the secret lies still hidden within these beautiful gemstones. I cannot help but think that Lake Superior agates chuckle, treasuring their secret of formation while the rest of us continue trying to solve the mystery.

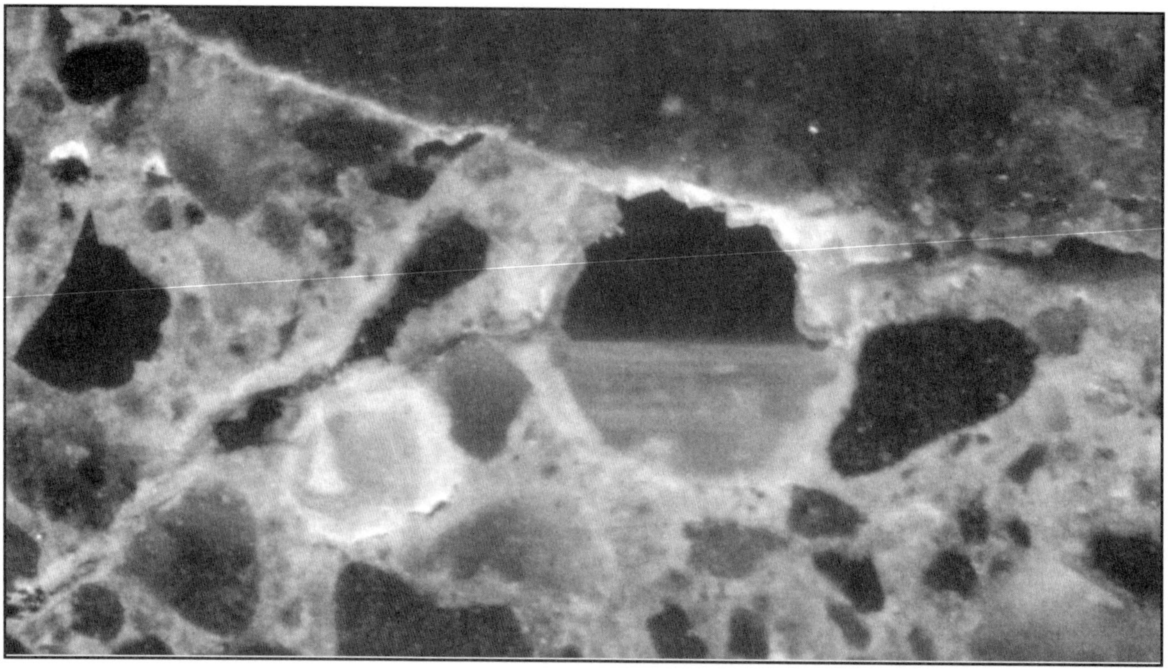

Horizontal layers of silica gel deposits within an air void in concrete that closely resemble water-level banding in agates. The gel was formed by reaction between the silicified limestone aggregate particle above the void and alkaline rich moisture (sodium and potassium in the cement paste). The resulting gel migrated through cracks formed by swelling from the expansive reaction and was deposited within the cracks and air void. Notice how a layer of gel lines the top of the void much like an agate and the top horizontal band is at the same elevation as a crack that appears to have drained away excess gel (30X).

This water-level silica gel deposit is partially filling an irregular shaped air void in concrete experiencing active alkali-silica reaction. Notice the thin gel layer lining the top of the void and drying shrinkage cracking in the bottom portion of the gel deposit. The bottom layers in water-level agates often display this polygonal type of crack pattern (mosaic agate) [45X].

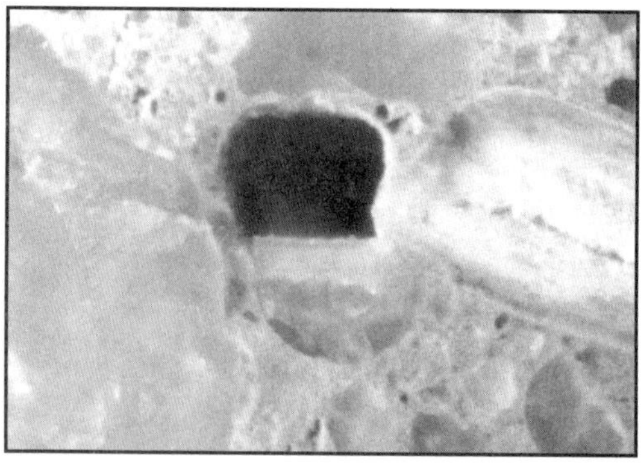

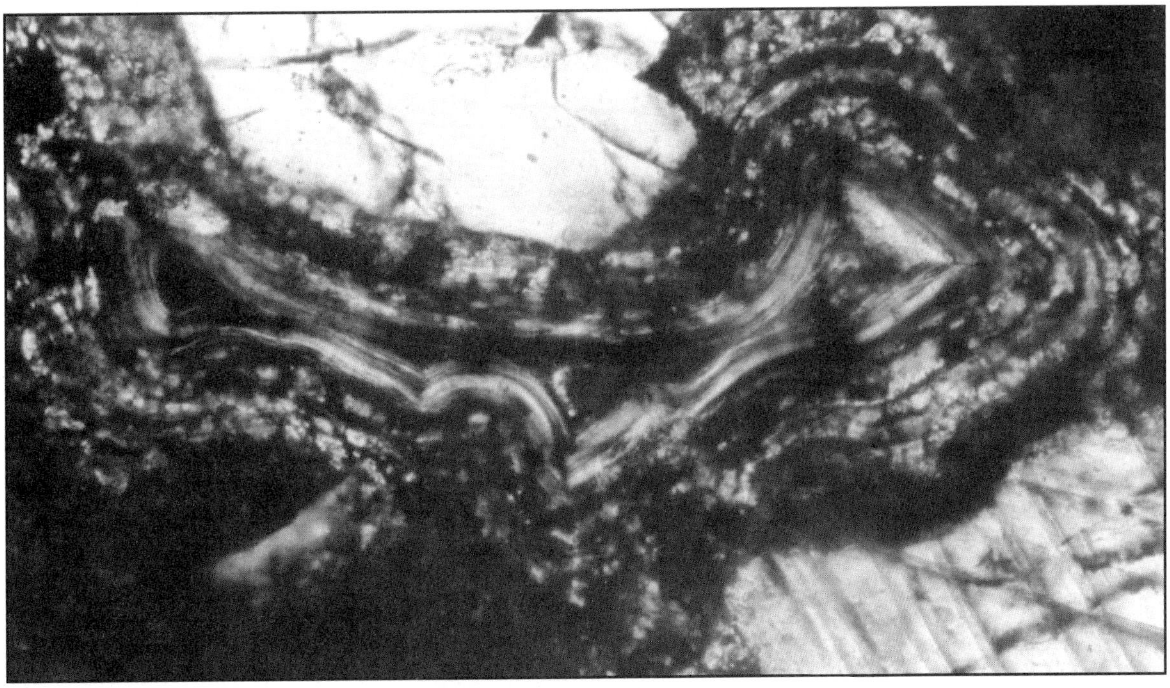

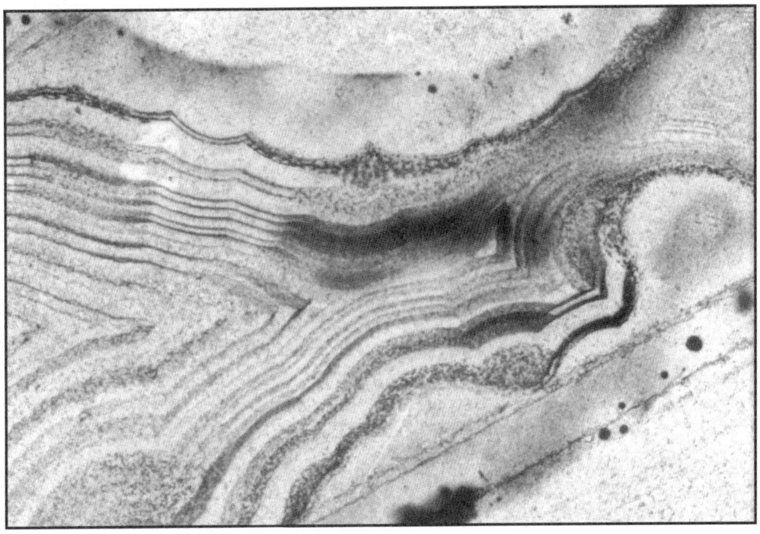

The agate-like pattern of the top photo was produced when layer after layer of silica was deposited within air void spaces in concrete upon repeated exposure it moisture (400X). The bottom photograph is of a Lake Superior agate (40X). Because these two thin sections (approximately 20-30 microns thick) resemble each other in appearance, perhaps they formed in the same way. Photographs taken under plane polarized light.

Essay: The First Lobe

Like prospectors, collectors of all kinds share common fantasies, from finding an extremely large or rare specimen, to locating a rich deposit of whatever the collector desires most. Lake Superior agate collectors are no different. When searching for agates, reality usually dominates the collector's thoughts so that he or she is not easily disappointed. When an exceptional specimen is found, the thrill and excitement are genuinely savored. But every collector has at some time probably indulged in a fantasy of discovering huge agates of rare beauty, or stumbling upon a special place where nearly every rock is an agate. These fantasies, of course, are just unattainable dreams—or are they?

If we study carefully the history of the transport and deposition of the Lake Superior agate by long-vanished continental glaciers, some interesting possibilities arise. Let's consider a few of them. Several reliable witnesses have told me of private collections of very large agates (from 3 to more than 10 pounds), each entire collection found by persons searching a single spot, such as a riverbank, a gravel pit, or an acre or two of farmland. The location of these spots remains a closely guarded secret, sometimes for many years. Reports of these unusual collections come from throughout Minnesota and western Wisconsin. But the most impressive collections are reported to belong to collectors in Iowa, Kansas and Missouri, areas much farther south than the generally identified hunting ground for the Lake Superior agate.

I have personally confirmed the existence of one such outstanding collection. The agates in William H. Boltz' collection include several specimens over 5 pounds, and all were collected in Topeka, Kansas, glacial drift (See Essay: The Boltz Agates, page 45). I have also seen and held a 21.62-pound banded Lake Superior agate that I now have in my collection. The stone was found by the late Ernest J. Counsell on his farm near New Haven, Iowa, in 1958. I have also seen two high-quality agates weighing 12 and 16 pounds that were found in farm fields near Austin, Minnesota. In addition, specimens weighing 7.41 and 11.96 pounds were collected in Iowa. All of these exceedingly large Lake Superior agates were found south of the line commonly believed to be the agate's southern limit. No doubt other examples exist that have yet to be confirmed.

Is there a reasonable explanation for these big agate "strays"? The geological history may provide one. Minnesota and Wisconsin based collectors generally believe that most agates are found in glacial sand and gravel deposits from the Wisconsin glaciation. These glacial sediments were deposited by the Superior lobe, a glacier that passed over lava flows in the Lake Superior region before stagnating at its southernmost boundary the St. Croix moraine, in what is now the Twin Cities. Because this glacier was the last agate-bearing ice to affect the present landscape, it follows that these deposits form much of the present land surface. Therefore, it is in these Wisconsin-age sediments that most agates are to be found.

It should be remembered, however, that at least three glaciations preceded the Wisconsin. The Nebraskan, Kansan, and Illinoian glaciations each sent lobes of ice across roughly the same areas. Each must have picked up and deposited agates along its flow-path, leaving behind a drift sheet that was subsequently buried beneath Wisconsin-age glacial material. Although all four glaciations left debris in overlapping geographic areas, the Nebraskan, Kansan, and Illinoian ice lobes traveled farther south and west than did the Wisconsin-age ice. These earlier glaciers reached northeastern Kansas and eastern Nebraska. Erosion has completely obliterated some of these deposits, but much of this older material remains. The limits of these older drift sheets have been fairly well mapped (Figure E-1).

The second part of a solution to this "big agate" puzzle requires a look back many hundreds of millions of years, to a time before any of the glacial periods. After the period when agates formed, weathering and erosion of the host lava began. In the subsequent eons, millions of agates were freed from their rock-walled prison and deposited in river and stream carried sediments. Eventually, as the worldwide climate turned colder the Great Ice Age began. Roughly two million years ago, the very first ice lobe of the Nebraskan glaciation crept into Minnesota. That lobe passed over the rich deposits of agates and carried them along on the initial trip south. At some point, the ice reached its southern extent in Nebraska, Missouri, and Kansas. Along with the sands and gravels it deposited, the glacier also left a rich trove of agates.

Although this scenario seems to explain how areas south of the generally accepted Lake Superior agate region came to abound in these stones, it does not account for the presence of an unusually number of very large vesicles and , consequently, large agates.

When the very first lobe of ice flowed across the agate-rich, weathered lavas of the Lake Superior region, its base would have become engorged with many large agates. These agates would have been carried and deposited in drift south of Minnesota. As seen in Figure E-1, the Nebraska-Age deposits were overridden and buried beneath later glacial debris. Erosion has since exposed intermittent patches of this older material. If collectors, like Bill Boltz, have stumbled upon such agate-rich hotspots, the stories of fantastic collections now thought to be fairytales could quite likely be true!

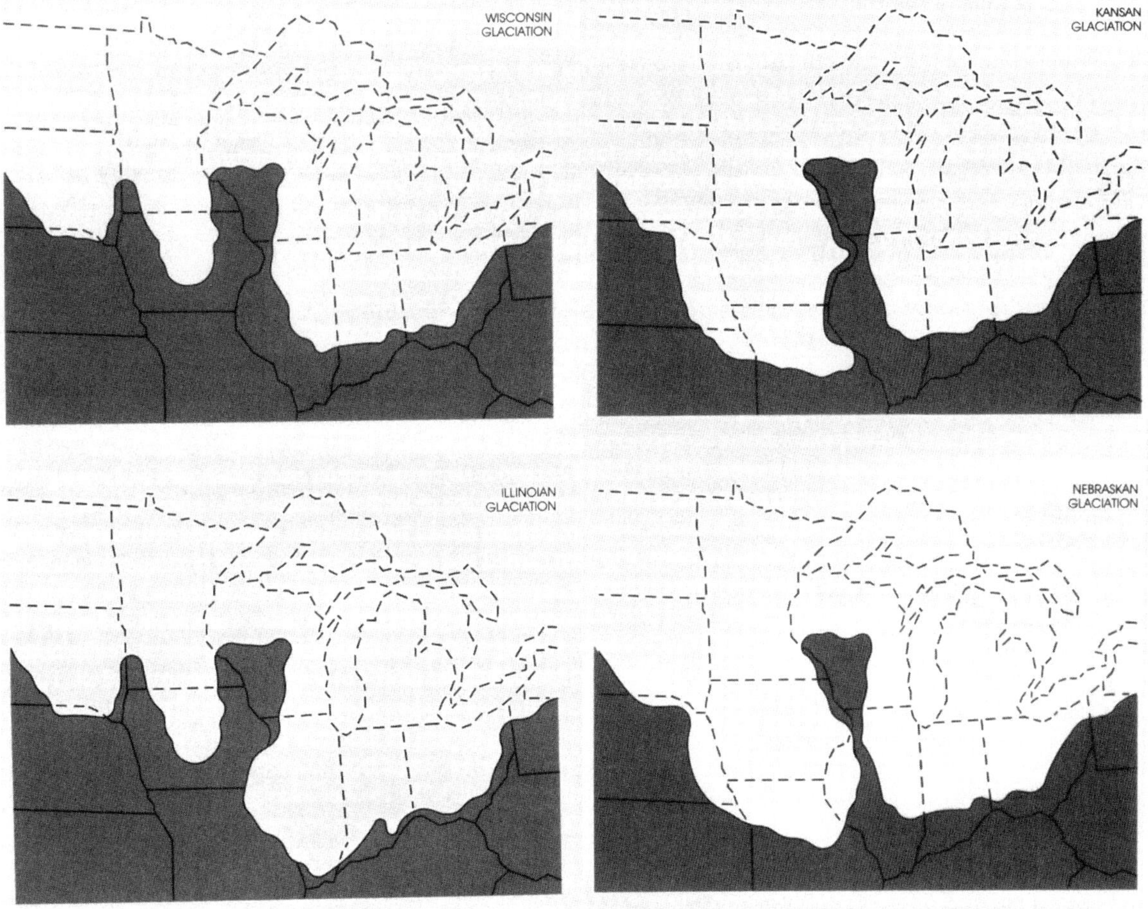

Figure E-1: The maximum-extent boundaries of the four classic glaciations that advanced during the Pleistocene Epoch (Great Ice Age).

Essay: The Boltz Agates

On of the truly enjoyable aspects of agate collecting for me has been meeting many interesting people. The characters who collect agates can be just as unique and colorful as the specimens they acquire. One of the true gems of the hobby passed away in December of 1992 at 84 years of age. Over 40 of those years were spent collecting Lake Superior agates and sharing the beauty of those rocks, and the knowledge he acquired, with others. The late William H. Boltz of Topeka, Kansas, was well known to many collectors. He often displayed his agates at rock shows and club meetings. E. L. Banion wrote an article about Lake Superior agates in Topeka that appeared in the April 1971 issue of Lapidary Journal. The article included photographs of many of Bill's finest specimens. I was fortunate enough to meet Bill and personally examine his wonderful collection.

The first time I contacted him was in 1985 when I was conducting research for the first edition of this book. I had heard about Mr. Boltz from other collectors who told me about the large Lake Superior agates he had collected in Kansas. At the time, I didn't realize that Lakers had been carried that far south. I knew that the glaciers had deposited material in those areas; it just never occurred to me that agates would be in those deposits. Bill and I talked about collecting in our respective areas and he offered to send me a copy of the Lapidary Journal with the article featuring his agates. I told myself that someday I would get down there to see him and his agates. I didn't think it would be nearly five years before I did.

In February 1990, the opportunity presented itself while driving back to Minnesota from a vacation in Arizona. Janet, Mike Carlson and I pulled a 28-foot motor-home into the Boltz driveway. Bill and his wife Helen kindly invited us into their home. He was thin, medium in build and was fighting a rather nasty cold. He hadn't told us that he wasn't feeling well, but I think he was excited about showing his rocks and sharing his tales. Several of his specimens were laid out on the kitchen table. I gazed at the table and was taken aback by the number of specimens, size and quality of his collection.

As we began to closely examine each agate, we noticed a similarity about many of them. It was obvious that they were Lake Superior agates, but something was different. Most of the agates appeared more weathered than the rocks we collect farther north. There was a greater frequency of fractures along with white bleached areas on many of the agates. The bleaching is believed to be caused by long exposure to the sun. In addition, a high percentage of the specimens appeared as fragments of larger agates that had been broken up. It mad sense that these agates should be in this condition for they had been carried the greatest distance by the glaciers. These agates were deposited during the middle Pleistocene, perhaps up to one million years ago, during the Kansan glaciation. The till and outwash of that glacier had been weathering for perhaps 1,000,000 years longer than the Wisconsin age lakers we collect in Minnesota, Iowa and Wisconsin (~15,000 years ago). Even though many of the specimens had been "beat up" by the glaciers, there were still some awfully big and beautiful ones he'd collected. He had several over two pounds with the largest being a 16-pound moss agate with a large, white bleached area on one side of the stone.

We eventually moved into the living room where he handed me, one at a time, some of his best finds. He told the story of how and where he found each agate. Anyone who has found a good agate can remember exactly when and where they found it. Right down to what they were wearing, what time of day it was, and what side of the specimen they saw first. Even at 81, Bill could recall every detail of each find. He relayed how he had always been interested in natural history while growing up. It wasn't until 1951, when a large flood in Topeka washed out some of the old glacial drift, that he found his first agate. From then on he was hooked. One of the best collecting areas was in what is now the southeast part of Topeka. During the 1950s, 1960s and 1970s this area was developed with primarily residential housing. As the grading of the land was performed prior to construction of a residence, Bill would scour the drift for agates. He amassed quite a collection in 40 years.

After we viewed his best agates, we sat down and he gave his slide presentation. It was a great show and at the end, as we prepared to leave, Bill didn't seem the least bit bothered by his cold; Lake Superior agates have that kind of effect on people. Our bumpy motor-home ride back to Minnesota went quickly as my mind was preoccupied thinking about the wonderful gems we had seen.

Bill never wanted to sell his agates, and his wish was that some day his collection would end up in a museum or university where many people could enjoy and learn from his specimens. In October of 1993 his wife Helen and two daughters, Mary Margaret and Elizabeth, donated portions of their collection to several institutions including the State of Minnesota. I was fortunate enough to represent the State and hand select roughly two dozen specimens that are now on display at the Agate/Geological Interpretive Center in Moose Lake. Those Lakers from Topeka were brought back closer to their birth place to tell their special chapter in the Lake Superior agate story. I think Bill would have wanted it that way.

CHAPTER 5
Where to Find Lake Superior Agates

Without a doubt the most fulfilling aspect of agate collecting is the challenge and joy of finding them in the field. The discovery of a beautiful Lake Superior agate produces the same sort of euphoria experienced by any other collector when finding a flawless specimen. Here is a guide to collecting that if followed with diligence and patience, can result in a beautiful collection.

The distribution of the Lake Superior agates is directly linked to the action of lobes of glacial ice that deposited the gemstones primarily into moraines and outwash associated with meltwater streams. Both kinds of deposits contain inter-bedded layers of sand and gravel; agates are commonly found in the gravel layers or beds. **Construction sites** often expose these gravel beds when initial bulldozing shapes the landscape. Excellent collecting, or "picking," can often be had at these sites after a cleaning rain washes the surface stones. Other areas where agates can be found include trails, driveways, graded roads, or anywhere glacial gravel is exposed at the surface.

While many fine agates are found at construction sites, the best place to find these exposed agate-rich gravel beds is in an active **gravel pit**. When a gravel pit is being worked, bed after bed of boulders, cobbles, sand, and gravel is exposed by shovels gouging large holes into the landscape. As the pit deepens, sand and rocks fall from the steep pit walls and accumulate at the base of the slope. This concentrated gravel and rock is called "the drop." The drop is one of the most desirable areas to "pick" or look for agates. Here one may find agates of all sizes including, perhaps, the rare "big one."

While these piles are undoubtedly the best areas to search for agates, caution is necessary. Walls of recently worked sand and gravel are very unstable and often cascade down in slides that can sometimes be enormous. Slides can occur in a split second without warning and travel at speeds in excess of 100 miles per hour. An unwary collector who does not exercise caution and common sense can be buried and suffocated almost instantly. Stay off the high banks and keep clear of steep, recently worked areas when looking for agates in such locations.

Another danger when searching in a gravel pit is boulders, which can roll down the slope without warning. These rocks can ricochet off other boulders and become potentially lethal projectiles. Remember, too, that gravel pits are private property, and having written permission from the owner to hunt agates is the only acceptable way to search in them.

One gravel pit activity that can greatly assist agate collectors is "crane dredging." A common operation in larger, well worked pits, crane dredging involves a large crane that dredges out gravel below the existing water table, creating a lake. The crane's bucket scoops out material from the depths of the lake and dumps the washed gravel into large piles. As dredging continues, the lake increases in size, as do the piles of removed material. These piles are an excellent source of large washed agates.

Active gravel pits are the best place to find Lake Superior agates. Many fine specimens have been found in this gravel pit located in central Minnesota.

A large front-end loader scoops out sand and gravel from the base of a bank in an "active" gravel pit.

Rocks and boulders of various sizes accumulates at the base of a gravel pit bank. This concentrated rock, which is an excellent place to find agates, is called the "drop."

Other good sources of agates within a gravel pit include the sorted gravels used as fill, decorative stone, and aggregate for concrete. These gravels offer excellent agates but are at the same time frustrating to hunters of large agates, because the rocks found in them are limited in size to the range of 1/2 inch to 2 inches in diameter. Furthermore, many of these agates are cracked, chipped, or mere fragments of larger stones mutilated by the "crusher," a large, belt-driven machine that crushes and grinds larger rocks and boulders down to a desired size. Nevertheless, these sorted piles are excellent places to search, because they are constantly supplied with new rock and are often very large, providing many fine medium-sized agates.

Searching for agates in decorative stone after it has left the gravel pit can also be very rewarding. **Decorative stone** is commonly used around residential homes and other buildings, parking lots, trees, bushes, and elsewhere. It's a mistake to take this landscape decoration for granted, since it is often loaded with unseen gems just waiting to be discovered. The Minneapolis-St. Paul area and suburbs have produced many fine agates, some as large as 1/2 pound. As construction and development continues in and around metropolitan areas, so will the placement of decorative stone and the discovery of Lake Superior agates.

Another good place to look for agates is along the shores of **Lake Superior and other lakes**. The beaches are best when picked after a storm or period of high winds. The large incoming waves stir up the rocks in the shallow water and wash agates up onto the beach. Many beaches along Lake Superior have been well searched, so finding agates there is particularly difficult, but there's no telling what may wash up after a nasty storm on the big lake.

A large crane with a drag-line bucket is pictured next to a pile of dredged out gravel taken from below the existing water table.

Rivers cutting through the countryside in Minnesota and Wisconsin, particularly those along the North Shore of Lake Superior, are another fine place to hunt the gemstone. The best time to pick is after a heavy runoff has subsided following a heavy rain or the spring thaw. Rivers and streams, lined with glacially derived material, will periodically free agates to be discovered along the freshly washed banks.

Perhaps the best river of all to search for agates is the Mississippi. Large gravel-bank deposits contain agates that were deposited when the river was many times larger than it is now. The deep river valley we see today was excavated by the vast torrent of water created when the glaciers melted away between 12,000 and 9,000 years ago. This swift current carried agates far downstream. In fact, agates have been found along the "Great River" as far south as Iowa, Missouri, and even Arkansas.

Many large agates have been found in the old rock piles created years ago by farmers clearing their land for farming. Agates weighing more than 10 pounds have been found in these rock piles. Areas such as Little Falls, Minnesota have a reputation for producing large agates, many from **farm-field rock piles**.

An eager agate collector (Michael Carlson in 1985) scans a pile of 1 1/2 inch-sized sorted gravel that is most commonly used as decoration rock.

When you have located a likely site, whether it's a gravel pit, a construction site, or a pile of stones, stop and take a look at all of the rocks in the area. The presence of many dark, well-rounded stones and boulders increases your odds of finding agates. These dark rocks are primarily volcanic rocks from the lavas in which the agates originally formed. Such rocks are part of the bedrock of the Lake Superior region that were eroded, transported, and deposited by the Superior lobe. Other glaciers entered Minnesota from different directions and deposited material very different from Superior lobe debris. Pale yellow limestone, light gray shale, and pink granite are rock types associated with the Des Moines lobe. This glacier entered Minnesota from the northwest shortly after the retreat of the Superior lobe and left drift that is generally devoid of agates (figure 5-1). In many places, Des Moines lobe material overlies Superior lobe material and agates are not found at the surface. If both dark volcanic rocks and lighter-colored Des Moines lobe materials are present, mixing has occurred, and agates can be found.

Decoration rock is most often found adorning homes and businesses. Occasionally, however, the agate-bearing rock is seen in other, unusual places, such as the roof of the Marriot Hotel in downtown Minneapolis.

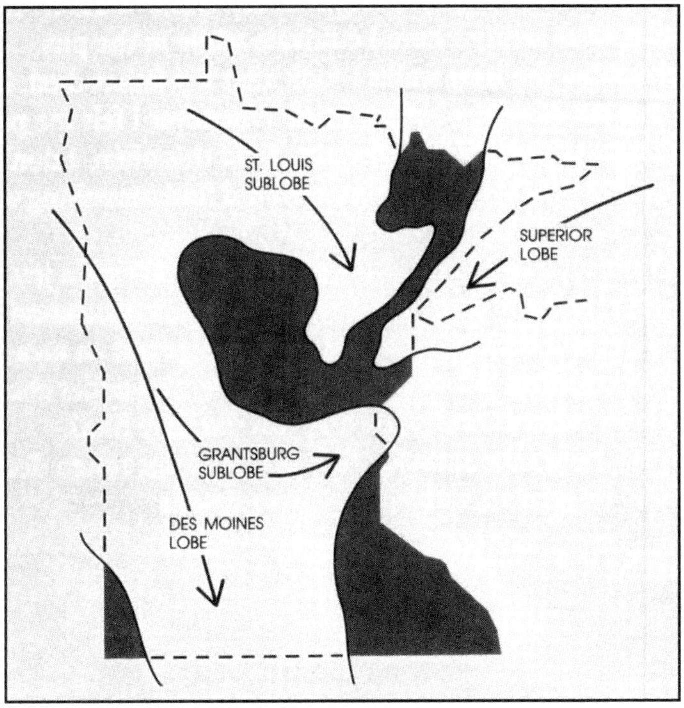

Two other sources where agates can be had, for a price, are rock shops and collectors. Several rock shops in Minnesota and Wisconsin sell Lake Superior agates as rough stones, polished pieces and attractive jewelry. Large rough agates are available almost exclusively through long-time collectors. The largest and most beautiful agates bring prices that range into the hundreds, and sometimes even thousands of dollars, and can be good investments. These large stones are quite rare and their beauty is captivating.

Finally, remember that the Lake Superior agate, even under the best of conditions can be very difficult to find. But once you have located a promising site, you have greatly increased you chances for a successful search.

Figure 5-1: The Des Moines lobe and its sub-lobes followed topographic low areas while moving through Minnesota. The ice reached its farthest southern extent at what is now Des Moines, Iowa. (Redrawn from *Minnesota's Geology*, Ojakangas and Matsch).

Essay: The Ups and Downs of Picking

Although the ultimate goal of picking agates is to find beautiful and interesting specimens, there are other pleasures to be derived from the hobby. I think most people would agree that many collecting sites offer beautiful scenery. The rivers emptying into Lake Superior are some of the most beautiful to be found anywhere, and no one can deny the magic of the lake's North Shore. Although agates are sparse along the lakeshore, the area is so beautiful that even if you don't find any agates, the search repays your effort. I also know a couple of agate pickers who bring their fly-rods when searching along rivers and streams. They always happen upon a special spot where the agates will have to wait for them to make a cast or two.

Even in gravel pits, the experience is enjoyable. Jackrabbits, fox, deer, ducks, and other birds abound. All you have to do is lift your eyes from the ground for a moment and see what's checking you out.

Perhaps the most fulfilling aspects of picking agates is just being out there. I often pick alone and never do I feel more relaxed. To find agates you need to take your time, so time eventually becomes unimportant. When I go picking I let my mind wander. Its good therapy, too; I honestly believe that what sanity I have I cultivate while in the pits.

I especially remember the long walks I took after my father died. There were many times when I felt like I was out of control with my grief. Whenever I felt the panic well up inside me, I would jump into my car and head for the pits. I did this often. I don't really recall if I found many agates during those particular outings, but I did find something very important, the time to heal.

To be honest, I must admit that picking agates is not always a joy. Some experiences can quickly sink a collector into the depths of despair. The biggest frustration for me is arriving at the pit, especially after a recent heavy downpour that has ripened an area for picking, and seeing the ultimate horror, footprints. When this happens to me, I wonder tow things: who was clever enough to beat me here? And what on earth did they find?

Finally, of course, there's the situation that calls for some tough decision, such as arriving at a gravel pit only to be greeted with specific instructions.

This unpleasant sign greeted the author as he approached a county gravel pit near Moose Lake, Minnesota.

Essay: Michipicoten Island Agates

For someone who has seen as many Lake Superior agates as I have, I thought I'd seen the gambit of what the gemstone had to offer. Boy was I wrong! For 27 years now my pursuit of the elusive Laker has been at times at a feverish pace. The hours spent in the field collecting and visiting other collectors are many. In that time I've become pretty sure that I had seen it all. On December 11, 1993 my favorite gemstone threw me a curveball I had a hard time catching. For the first time, my chance came to examine Lake Superior agates from Michipicoten Island. This island is located roughly twenty miles off the Ontario shoreline in the northeastern portion of the Lake Superior. What makes these agates found here so special is that they are colorful, large, and unlike glacially deposited agates, are found inside their host rock.

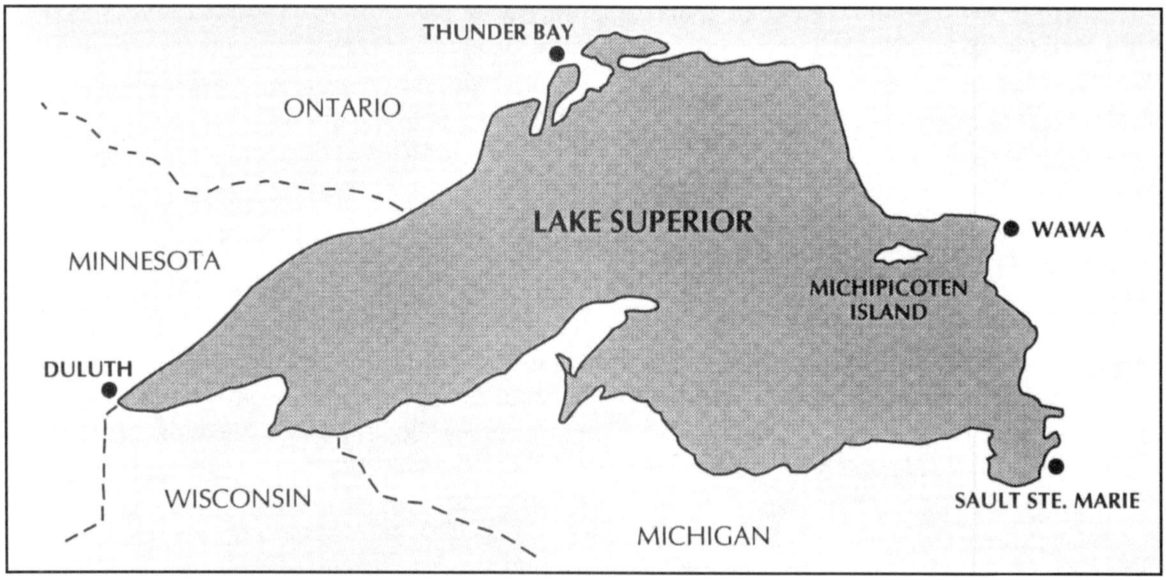

Figure E-9-1: Michipicoten Island is located in the northeast corner of Lake Superior roughly 40 miles west of Wawa, Ontario, Canada.

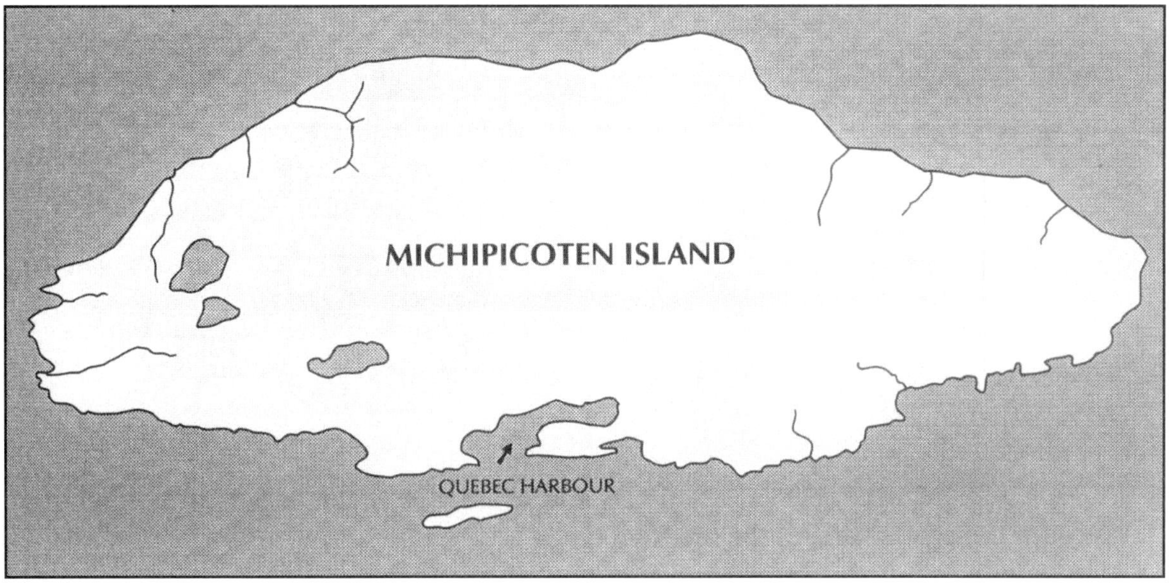

Figure E-9-2: Because of the unpredictable weather and rugged shoreline, the only safe mooring is in Quebec harbor at the south-central part of the island. The dimensions of the island are 16 miles long by 6 miles wide.

I first learned about Michipicoten Island agates in 1989. Someone told me about them while tailgating at the Moose Lake show. I remembered being told of huge red and white nodules were supposedly over 100 pounds. At first I dismissed the stories as fantasy. But when told by another person whose opinion I respected, I slowly became a believer.

I was even invited to take a trip up there, which someday I may do. A couple of summers ago, a fellow collector that I know quite well took a trip up to Michipicoten Island. He said the agates were there alright, but the trip nearly killed him. He said the water on the lake was so rough, that they nearly capsized several times getting there. They had even tried to collect a few specimens, but the island and its hard and dense lava would not give them up. My initial desire to see this agate wonderland soon dissipated when the realities of such an adventure sunk in. I've been in Lake Superior many times and the numbing cold has a sobering effect on those who choose to challenge her.

The family I met that December day accepted and met the challenge several times beginning in August 1962. Clayton and Alice Braun made the trip with their children, Clayton Jr., Jeanne, Gary, and David 6 times over a period of 22 years. At the time of my visit, Clayton Sr., was not there to tell me of his experiences. He died in 1984, but his wife and eldest son were kind enough to share their adventures. When I arrived early for our appointment at the quiet, well-kept farm in Central Wisconsin, I had to wait for Alice to return from some errands. While sitting in my pickup, I tried to imagine what the agates I'd heard so much about would look like. Secondly, I wondered about how much work it took to get them out of the basalt matrix they were encased in. My colleagues and I have only known collecting agates out of gravel deposits and sorted rock piles. The glaciers had already done the hard work. By the time Alice and her son Clayton arrived, curiosity had the better of me.

As they invited me into their home, I spotted the "rock room" right away just inside the door. I was slightly stunned as I entered the small room and saw the walls lined with shelves up to the windows with dozens of agates of all sizes. Many of the agates were still partly or completely encased in their host basalt. Most of the agates were faced polished showing brilliant color and attractive banding patterns. At first, I had a hard time believing what I was seeing. Never had I seen so many large, spectacular specimens in one collection all collected by the same individual or family. I examined each specimen carefully, and gradually, my awe was replaced by more logical thinking.

I began to see some similarities unique to these agates. The first thing was that two dominant and distinct color schemes were present. Most of the agates, roughly two thirds, were comprised of some variation of glassy red and bluish gray colors with bright white banding. The other common type was a deep orange to brown colored, finely banded "paint" agate. A few specimens were shades of gray and white, some with excellent shadow effect. Br far most of the agates were of the first two types.

Other unique aspects of the agates were their shape, frequent fractures and presence of crystalline calcite within the agates. The dominant shape of the agates was as flat veins or nodules, many with an asymmetric wedge shape. The fractures were probably induced during the collecting process, but many corresponded with joints and fractures in the host rock. It was strange indeed to see the well developed, white calcite crystals in many of the specimens. I also felt a strange satisfaction seeing clear proof of the material producing crystal impressions commonly observed on glacial agates.

Clayton Braun Sr. with his sons Gary (far left) and David at their campsite near the lighthouse on Michipicoten Island in 1965. (Photo courtesy of Alice Braun)

After my initial review of the agates, I tore myself away to spend time visiting with Clayton and Mrs. Braun. They recalled with fondness their trips to the beautiful island. They chartered both boats and airplanes out of Wawa, Ontario, Canada for the 10-day or so long trips. They told of camping, canoeing, long hikes, and hard work. I could relate to Clayton and his aggravation with the mosquitoes and black flies he recalled and

My lovely 13-year-old daughter, Amanda Wolter, took this photograph of Lake Superior agates that I have found or acquired since 1994. Most of these agates were collected since that time and serve as proof that there are many more big and beautiful agates yet to be found.

I took this photograph of my collection of Lake Superior agates in 1994, and it graced the cover of the Second Edition of this book. I also used this image to make a poster and a jigsaw puzzle. In 2004, the Minnesota Department of Natural Resources asked for permission to use this picture, and the eye agate image, on coffee mugs to help generate money for preservation of state parks. I was more than happy to grant that permission.

Since I took this picture in 1994 and used it for the cover of my Third Edition of this book, the largest single eye on a Lake Superior agate was found. It measures over 2 ¹/₈" in diameter. (See page C17.)

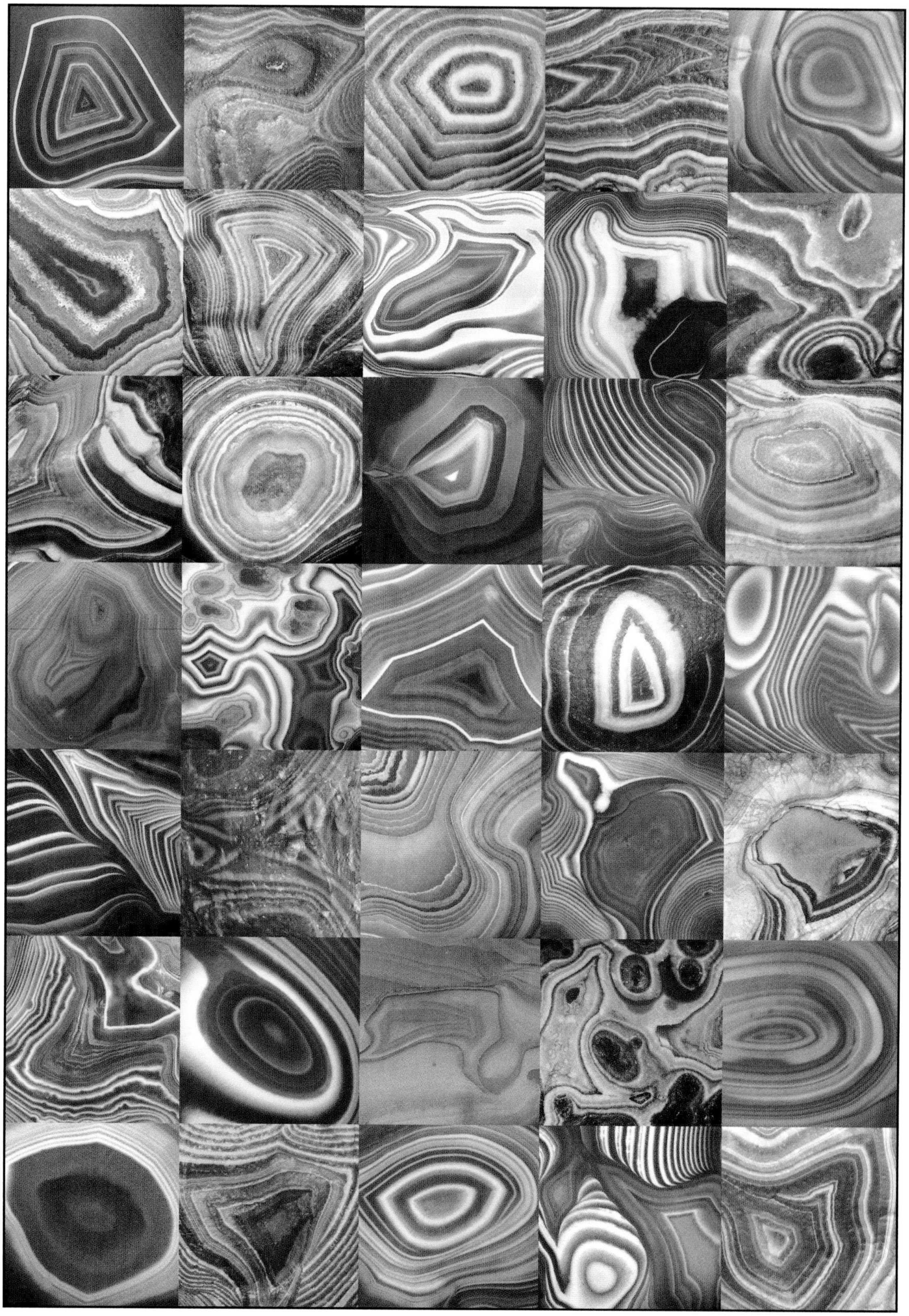

Minneapolis collector, Charlie White, assembled this beautiful montage of photos that illustrate the myriad of colors and patterns found in Lake Superior agates.

These two interesting agates look as though they could have originated from the same agate. Cabochons made from Lake Superior agates can be used in rings, belt buckles, bolo ties, and other types of jewelry, such as this watch fob with the compass and square, symbolic of Freemasonry, that was made in the 1920s. I found this Native American arrowhead made from Lake Superior agate in the J. B. Brower collection at the Minnesota Historical Society archives. Many agates found by Natives ended up in burial mounds that were excavated by archaeologists in the 1800s.

I've never been big on seeing things in agates, but I was totally amazed at how much the pattern on this 0.19-pound agate looks like the tongue logo of the legendary rock band The Rolling Stones.

These three fantastic agates that are now in my collection once belonged to the renowned collector Maynard Green of Grand Meadow, Minnesota. I first saw these monsters when I visited Maynard and his wife, Amy, in 1985. Left to Right: 4.92, 2.47, and 6.16 pounds.

One of the prettiest red-and-white "Candy-stripers" I've ever seen is this 1.88-pounder (left). I acquired it in a trade from long-time Lake Superior Agate collector Harold Johnston of Rice Lake, Wisconsin, in 1991. I named the red, white, and blue 2.50-pounder found in 1958 by Tom Olson the "Patriotic" agate (middle). This classic, tight-banded, brilliantly colored 1.70-pounder was spotted by a farmer who was on his tractor at his farm near Foley, Minnesota, in 1987 (right).

George Flaim owned all four of these stones when I first met him in the spring of 1984. From left to right the agates weigh 2.52, 2.12, 2.14, and 1.68 pounds.

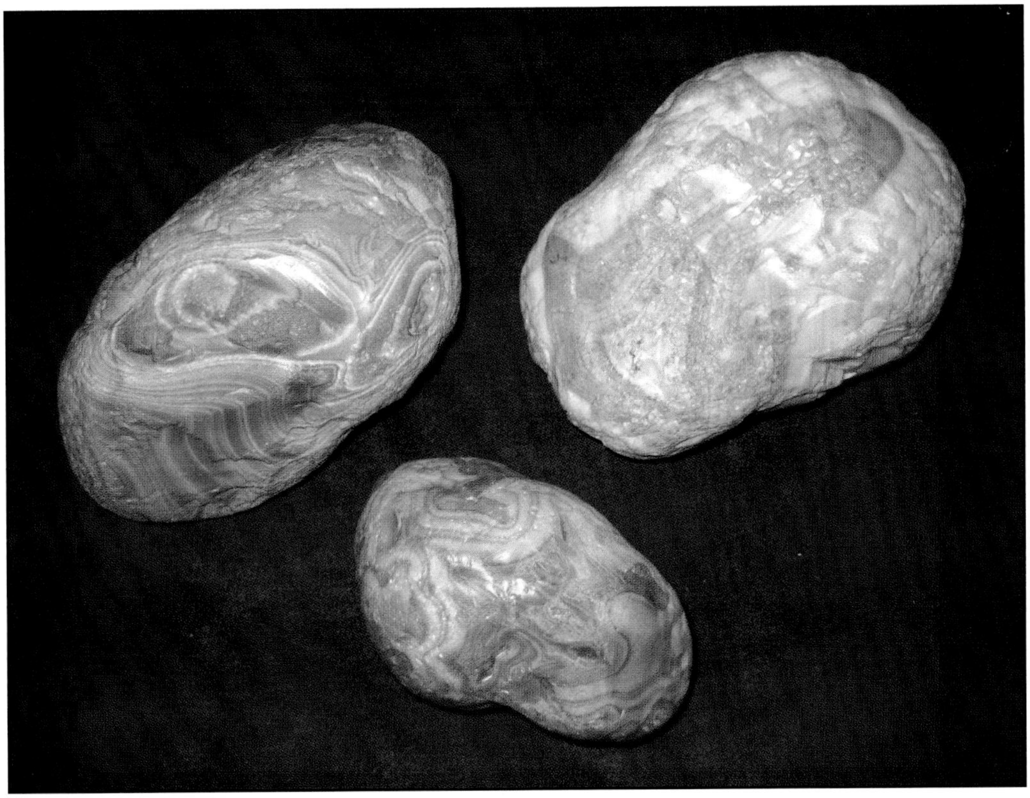

These agates from the Charlie White collection illustrate the amazing variation of colors that can be found in Lake Superior "paint" agates. From left to right, the agates weigh 3.64, 1.79, and 4.38 pounds.

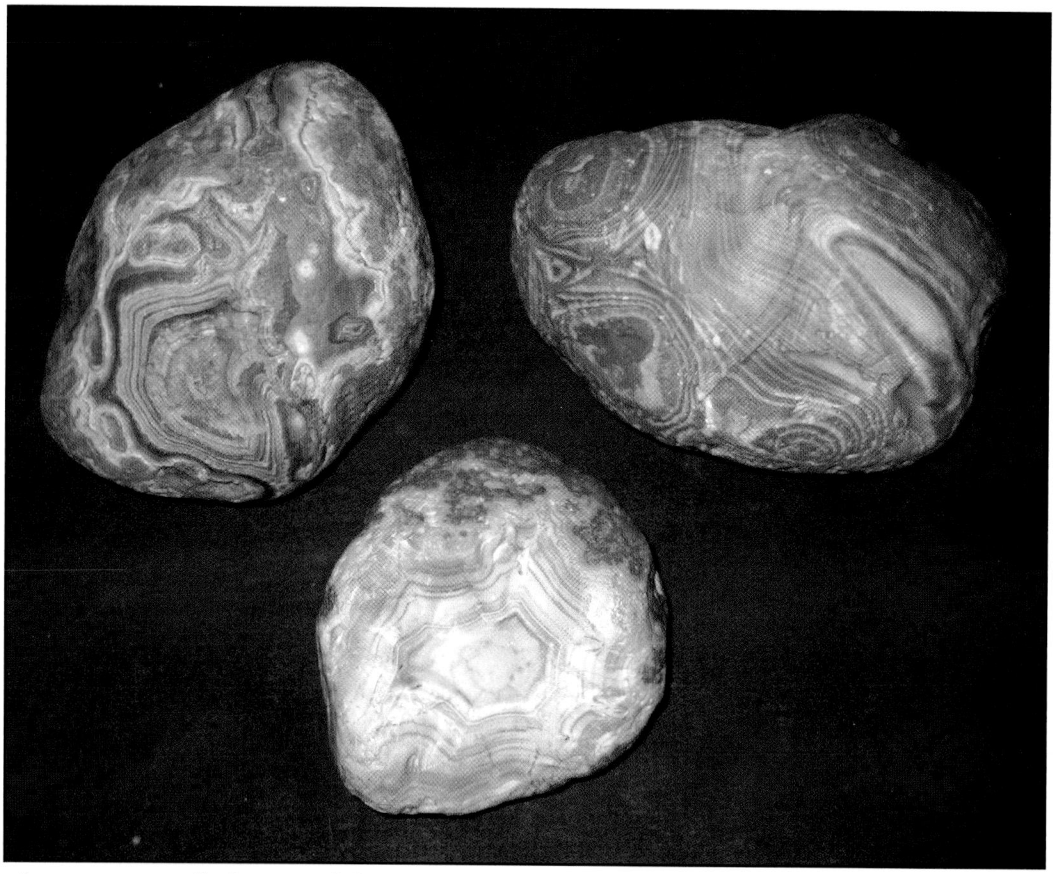

Here's three more great "paint-stones" from my collection that weigh 3.45, 1.29, and 3.66 pounds, respectively.

These two beauties were found by Dylan Newman (left) and Carlyn Iverson (right) and weigh 1.20 and 1.59 pounds, respectively.

These specimens might be two of the best red-and-white Lakers you will ever see. The 2.22-pound specimen on the left was found in a farm field near Long Prairie, Minnesota, and the 1.70-pounder on the right came from the Maynard Green collection and was found in Central Minnesota. Both agates were found in the 1960s.

The beautiful wind-polished 3.06-pound stone on the left was found by a farmer while tilling his garden near Avon, Minnesota, in June of 1988. We affectionately call this agate "Bulldog Deluxe" because of its big, bold, and concentric face. This great-quality, fine-banded 3.59-pounder on the right was found by George Flaim along the shore of Island Lake in Northern Minnesota, in about 1970.

The bold, red-and white banded 4.42-pound specimen on the left was found by a farmer in his field near Sobieski, Minnesota, in April of 2000. The 3.85-pound specimen on the right was found near Pease, Minnesota, sometime before 1980.

These two beauties were voted into the Top Ten rough Lake Superior Agates of all time. The 4.21-pound specimen on the left is called "Jingle Bells" and was found by David Stodola in the sandy gravel of a golf course that was under construction near Cloquet, Minnesota, in 1988. The "Engagement Agate" on the right weighs 5.75 pounds and was found by a Boy Scout walking along the beach at Island Lake, Minnesota, sometime around 1930.

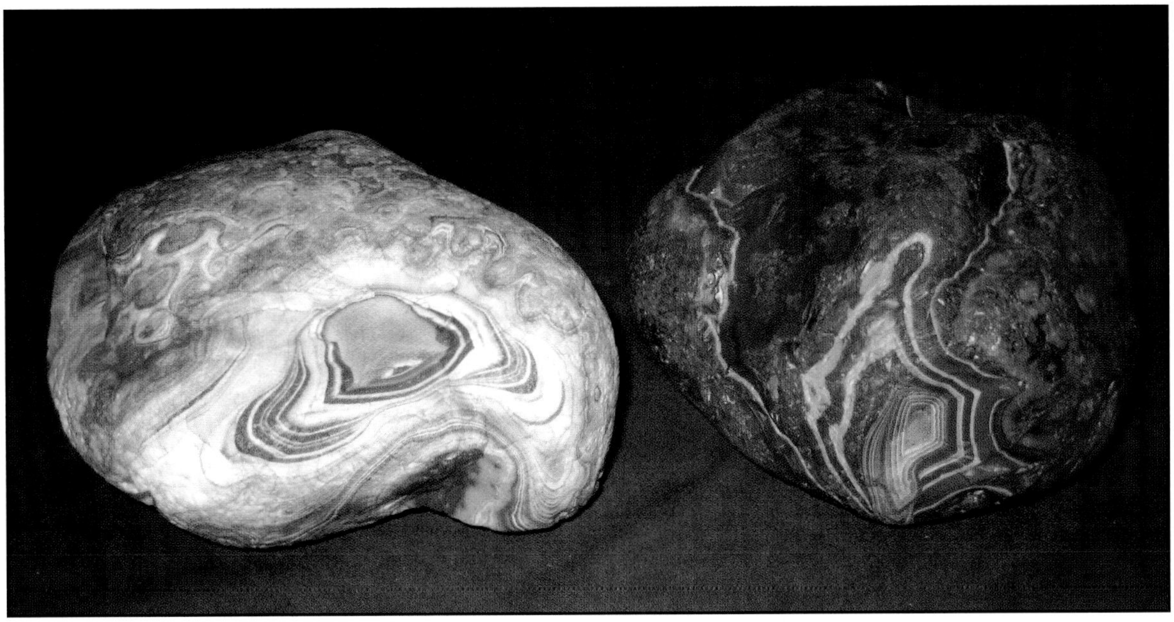

The 6.38-pound "Moore Agate" (left) was found by Jim Moore in a farm field near Balsam Lake, Wisconsin, in the mid-1940s. Lyle Berghuis found the 6.38-pounder on the right while picking agates with his 10-year-old daughter in a gravel pit near Milaca, Minnesota, in 1972.

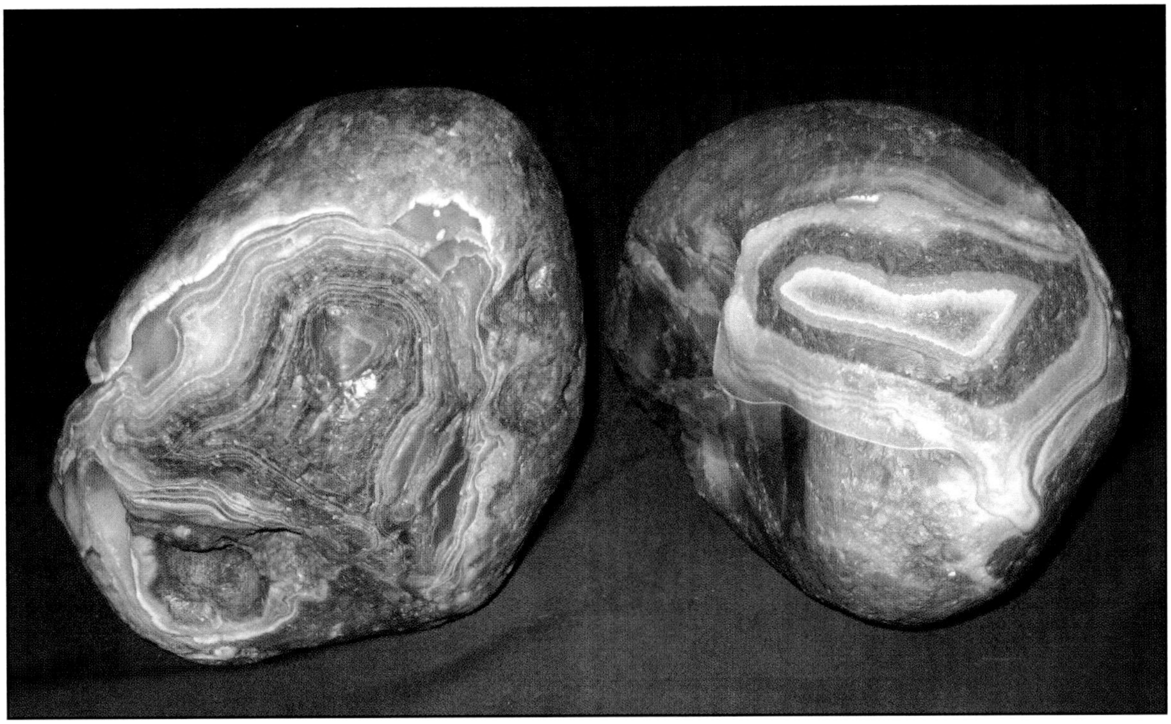

The 8.51-pound specimen on the left was reportedly found in a farm field near Pine River, Minnesota, in 1970. John Putzier spotted the 7.87-pound behemoth on the right while doing landscape work in Stillwater, Minnesota, in 1994.

The fantastic-quality 10.25-pounder on the left is arguably the finest big Laker ever. Nina Cox found the big agate while she was walking in a field with her husband, sometime before 1921. Until the day she died, at age 93, Nina believed that what she had found was a petrified ham. The 9.04-pounder on the right was recognized as an agate after it spent decades in a rock foundation wall in Wisconsin.

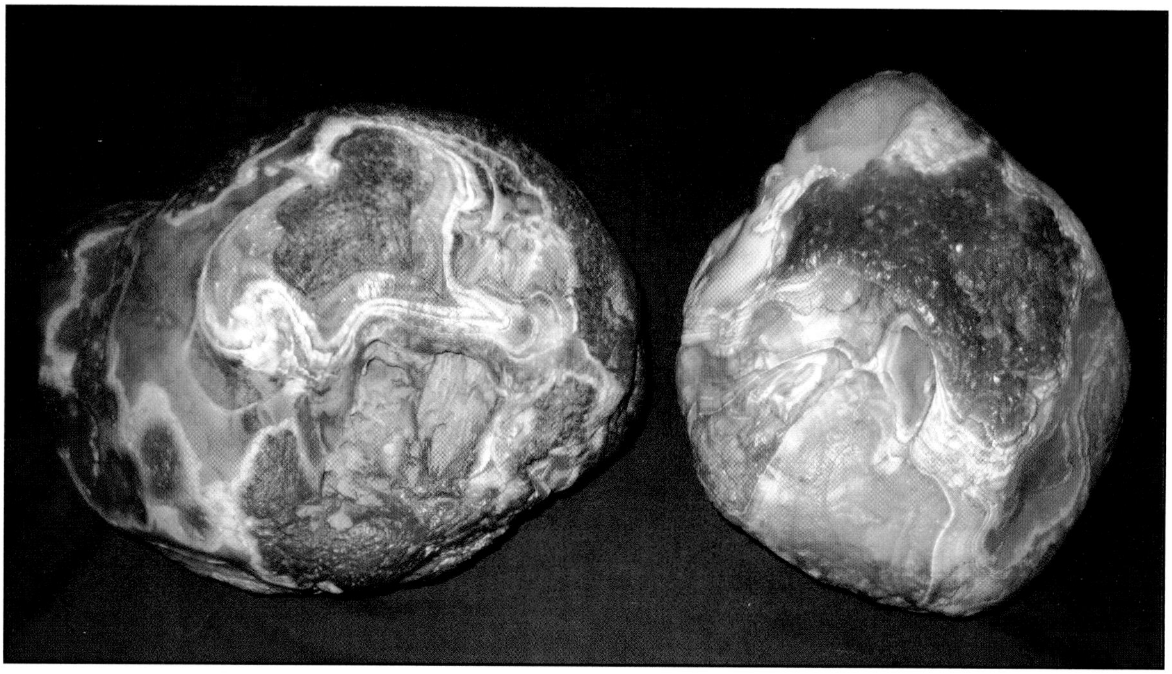

Ernest J. Counsell found the 21.62-pounder at left on his farm near New Haven, Iowa, in 1958. This specimen is the largest complete fortification Lake Superior agate found in glacial drift to date. The 14.75-pound specimen on the right was used as a doorstop at a farm near Pine City, Minnesota, where it was found in 1925.

These examples of siliceous (quartz-rich) rocks that are not Lake Superior agates were graciously provided by University of Wisconsin Eau Claire professor Todd Hosteger, and include three examples of silicified limestone (upper right), silicified fossil coral (lower right), iron-stained crystalline quartz (bottom middle), banded iron formation (lower left), and multi-colored jasper (upper-middle left). The biggest non-agate is Bud Grant's 6-pound silicified limestone "Leaverite."

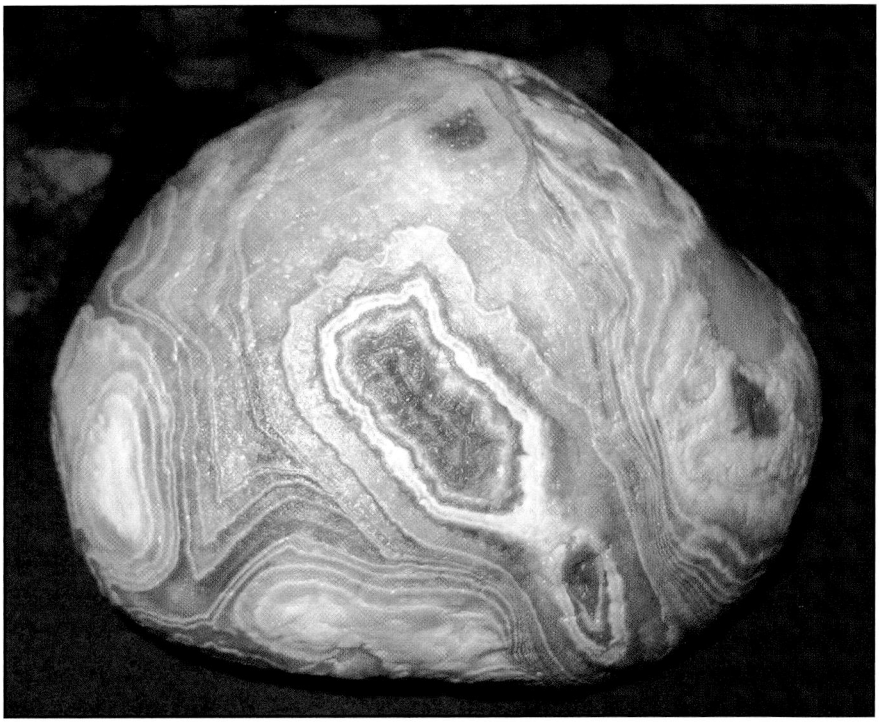

It took eight years to finally track down Jon Morell, who eventually sold me the 2.74-pound, white-and-red Floater he found in a gravel pit near his home in St. Cloud, Minnesota, in June of 2006.

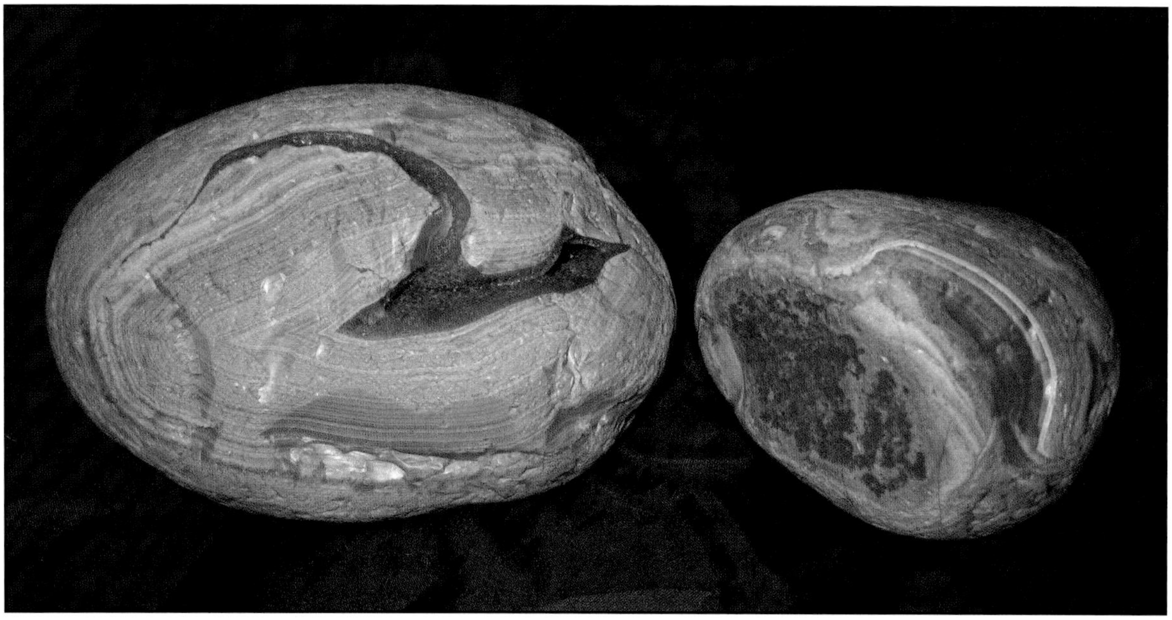

As fate would have it, the next time George Twardzik dove with his wife, Lisa, at the spot where the weather didn't cooperate during our *Cash & Treasures* dive, they found these two beautiful paint-stone agates. The show's host, Kirsten Gum, and I might have found the 2.16- and 1.14-pounders if we have been able to get there!

The next several photos show agates that have two great sides exposed. This spectacular 1.65-pounder was found on a farm near Buckman, Minnesota.

Jim Wright found this 1.72-pounder with two great faces while picking agates along Highway 33 near Cloquet, Minnesota, in 1994.

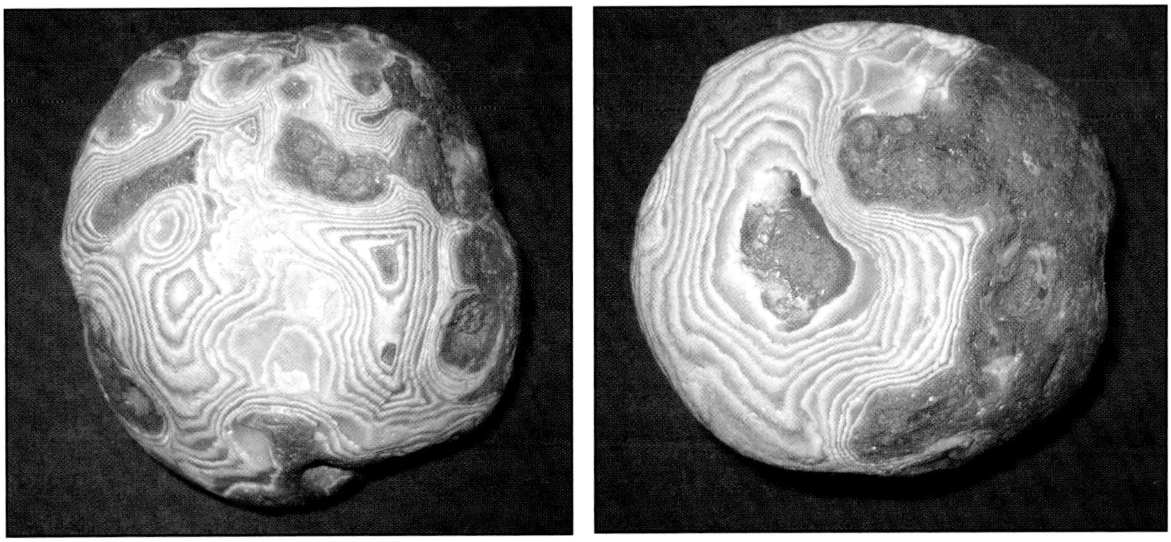

Craig Litchy found this 1.94-pounder in a gravel pit near Duluth, Minnesota, in the summer of 1997.

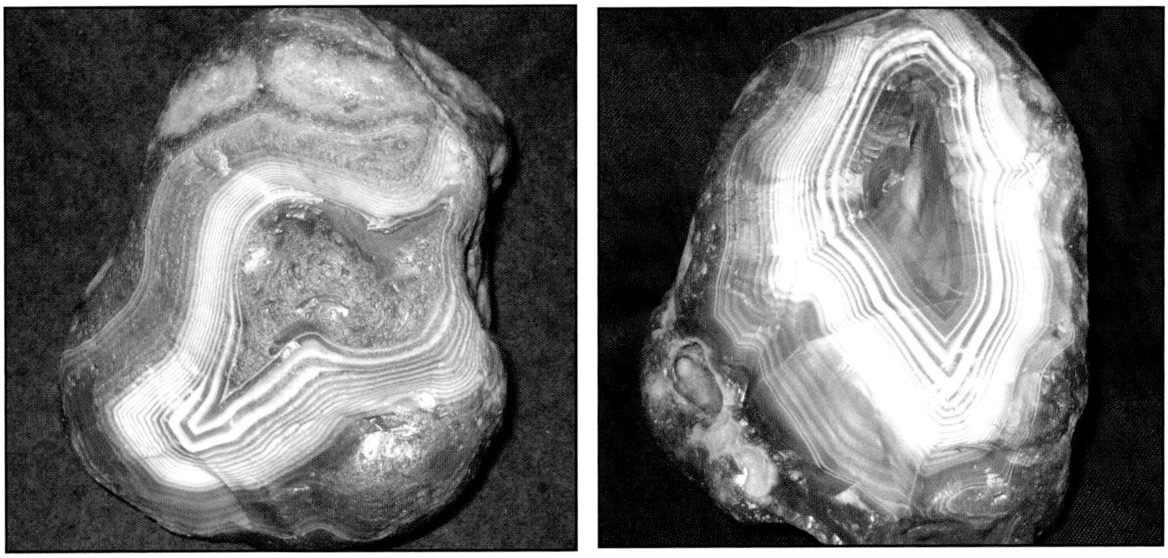

This beautiful 2.15-pound red-and-white Lake Superior agate was found by Rudolph Halderson when he worked on the Sawbill Trail near Grand Marais, Minnesota, in the 1930s.

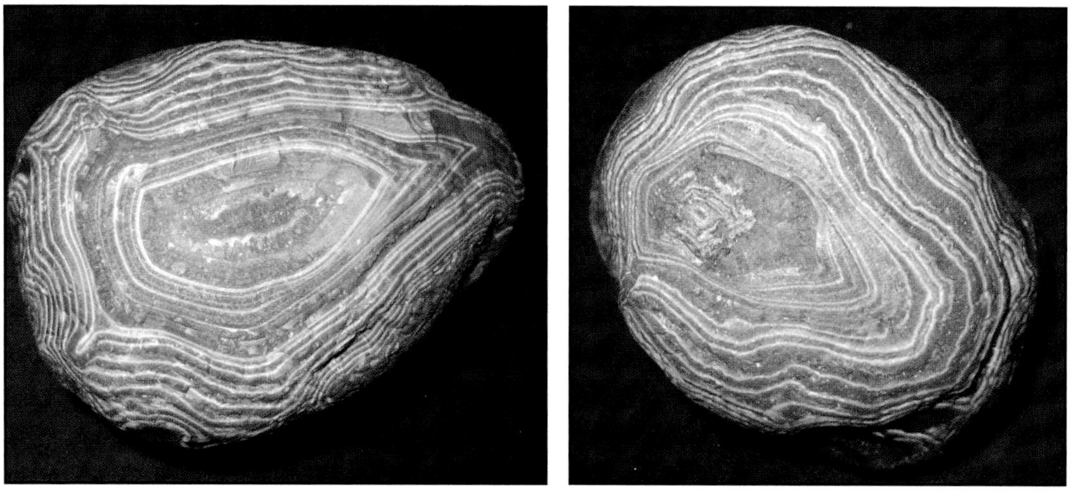

Few agates exhibit such richly colored red-and-white banding as this 2.63-pound specimen.

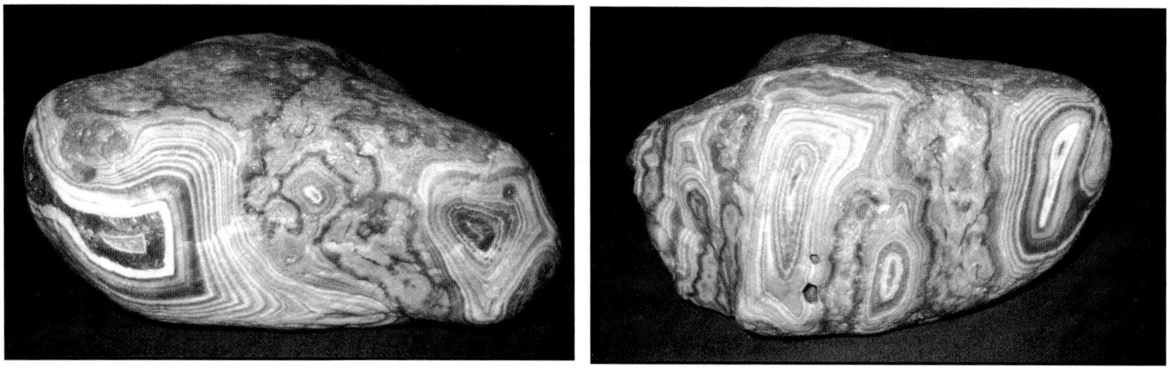

Al Holmes nearly threw this 2.50-pound beauty into a swamp while walking along a gravel road near Goodland, Minnesota, in 1985.

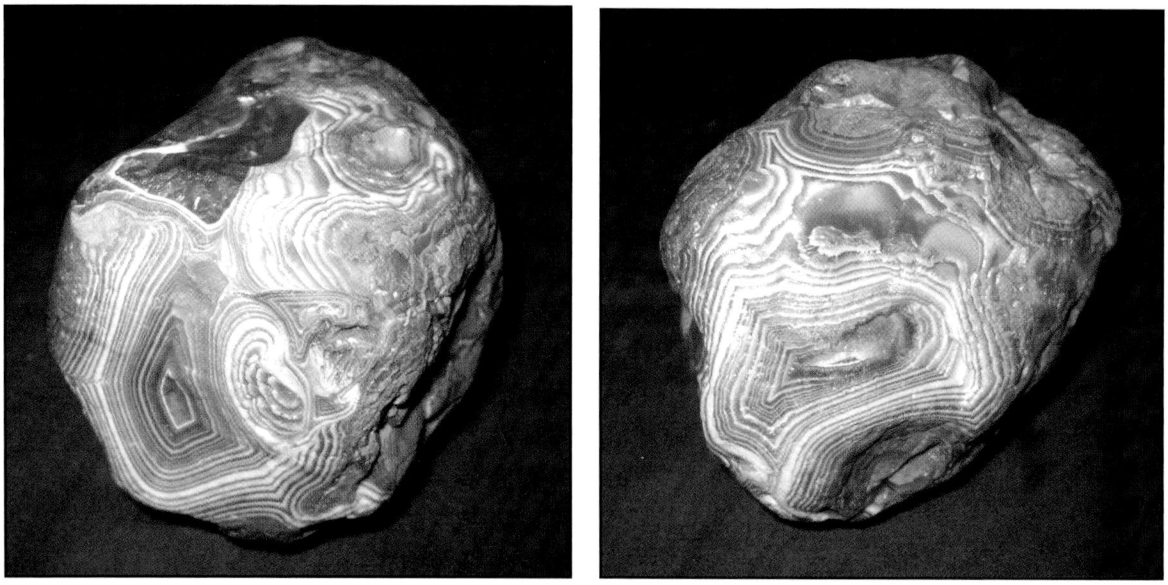

Charlie Clark found this 2.52-pound stone near Clear Lake, Wisconsin, in 2000.

The current record-holder for the largest single eye on a Lake Superior agate is 2 1/8 inches in diameter on this 0.69-pound specimen that was found near Aitkin, Minnesota.

This perfectly water-washed 0.77-pound agate was found in a gravel pit by Roderick Kuhlmey, near Royalton, Minnesota, in 2001. Roderick affectionately named the agate "God's Eye."

Rarely does an agate exhibit both wind-polished texture (shiny areas) called ventification, and a smooth texture from extensive water transport. In this beautiful 0.89-pound specimen, the wind polish occurred first, and then the agate was "water-washed."

Long-time collector John Moin traded this striking 1.41-pound agate to Charlie White in 2005.

This terrific 1.67-pound paint-stone was found by Rick Craw in a gravel pit near Cloquet, Minnesota, on November in 2005.

Cliff Donais sold me this 1.50-pound agate in 1983, and to this day, it is still one of my favorites.

A gravel pit worker found this 1.66-pound stone after it had been dredged out of the Mississippi River in Cottage Grove, Minnesota, in 1998.

The St. Cloud, Minnesota, area produced this super "Hamburger"-shaped 2.13-pounder.

I bought this 2.24-pounder from my long-time agate-picking friend, Michael Carlson, at the 2007 Moose Lake Agate Days Gem and Mineral Show.

Fellow agate collector Wayne Davis bought this richly-colored 2.52-pound "Sandwich" style specimen from a farmer who found it in his field near Malmo, Minnesota, in the summer of 1995.

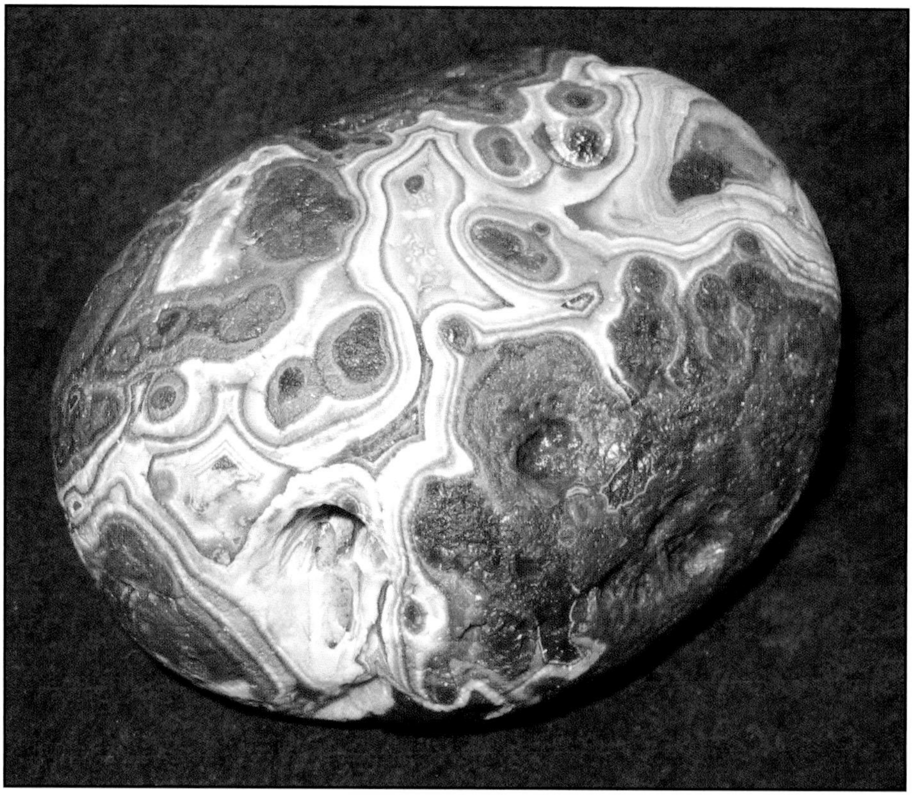

Jim Rodeski found this 2.69-pound agate while helping a neighbor dig fence post holes near Swanville, Minnesota, on June 12, 2004. The wild pattern on this brilliant red-and-white-colored stone inspired the name "Brush Fire."

This fine-banded 3.16-pounder was found by Jackie Vance in a flower garden outside her home in Brook Park, Minnesota, in October of 1998.

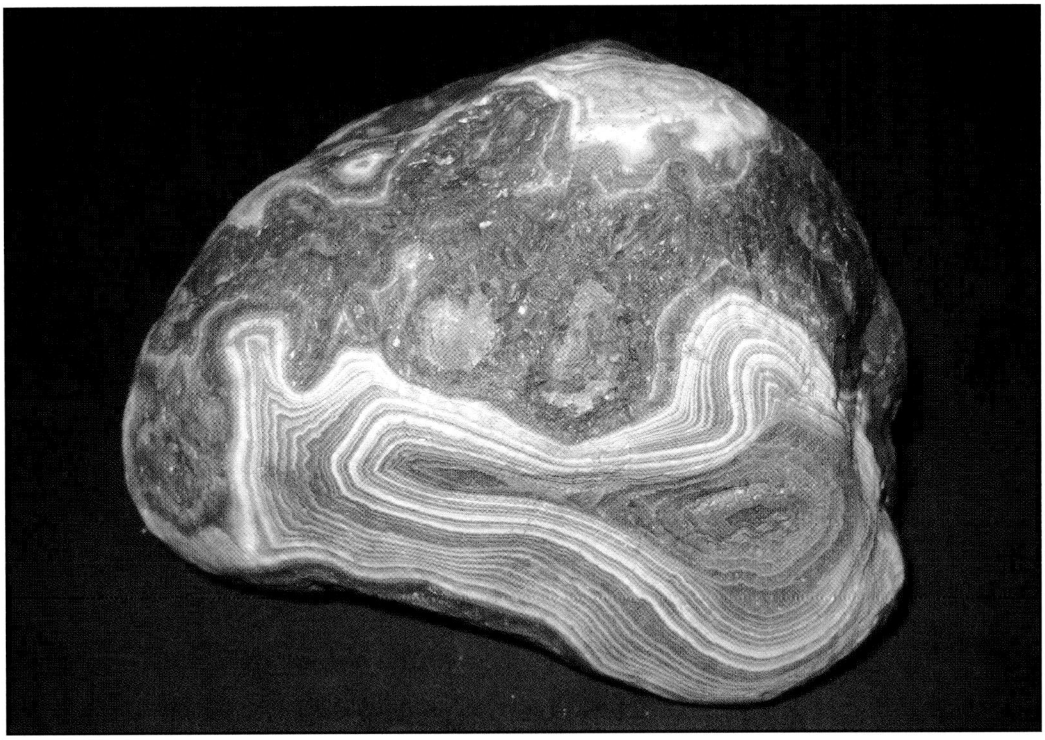

David Kirkorkian found this 4.02-pound agate while walking his dog in a gravel pit near Scanlon, Minnesota, in 1994. If you turn this photograph clockwise 90 degrees, you'll see the outline of a "Howling Wolf."

Another gravel pit worker found this beautiful, 3.65-pound fine-banded Floater near the Twin Cities. I've picked agates for over 25 years in this pit, and I've never found an agate this big with such high quality.

Matt Howard was sixteen years old when he found this 4.58-pound agate while walking into a gravel pit near Saginaw, Minnesota, in 2001. My heart started racing and my face went flush the first time I saw this agate at Terry Roses' "Fragments of History" store in Duluth, Minnesota, where I purchased it from Matt. This spectacular stone might be the finest big Lake Superior agate I've seen in my life—so far!

The pattern on this 4.74-pounder reminds me of the "Batman" signal from the famous comic book character's television series. Twelve-year-old Cody Post found this agate in a gravel pit near Pierz, Minnesota, on August 19, 2006.

The wild pattern on this 5.35-pounder found in a gravel pit near Duluth, Minnesota, is reminiscent of a bowl of spaghetti.

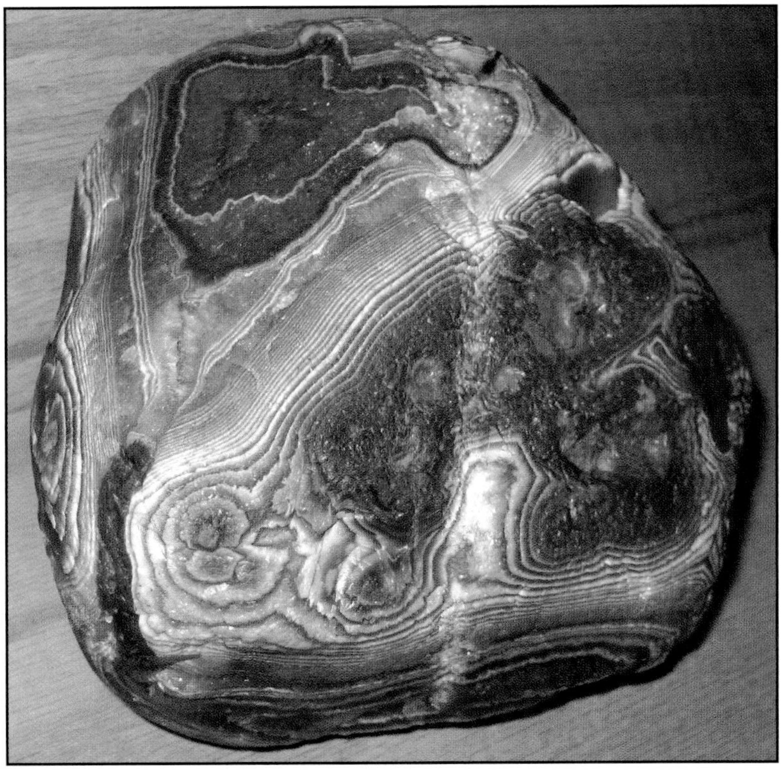

The shallow-pecked groove running vertically through the center of this incredible 7.41-pounder was made by Native Americans in the distant past. This agate was found along the creek bank below Minnehaha Falls in south Minneapolis, Minnesota, in the fall of 1932.

Willie Thomson pulled this giant 11.15-pounder from a rock pile in a gravel pit near Isle, Minnesota, in October of 2007. Long-time collector and friend, Bruce Peddle, spotted the agate on Ebay and told me to check it out. That same evening, Willie and I consummated a deal for the agate.

I found this 0.34-pound agate in Maple Grove, Minnesota, in November of 2001, and then decided to polish it in 2007. This specimen has unique green colors with a large, lavender-colored eye exposed in cross-section.

The agate voted the number *ten* polished Laker is a striking peanut butter-orange-and-white-colored 1.43-pound paint-stone.

Bill Steffes polished and submitted the number *nine* agate that weighs 0.88 pounds and has an absolutely stunning red-and-white pattern.

Bob Lynch submitted this photograph of his 1.33-pound, fine-banded beauty that was voted the *eighth* best polished Lake Superior agate. (Photograph by Robert Lynch.)

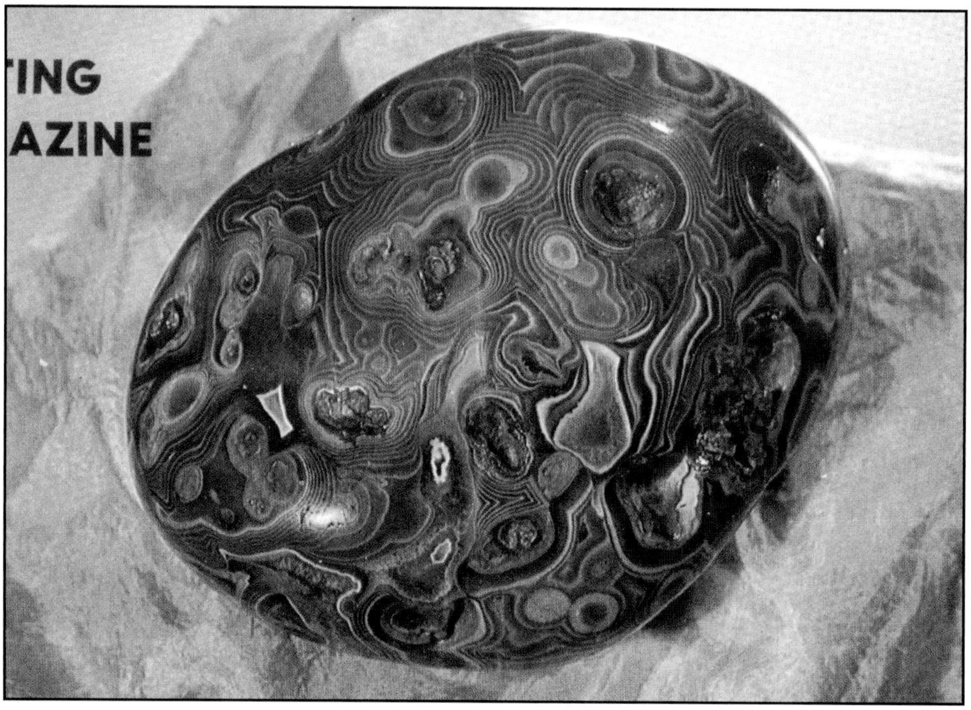

Number *seven* on the Top Ten Polished Laker list is a spectacular 4.15-pound specimen found by Charlie Smart near Pillager, Minnesota, in the 1960s. This gorgeous, tumble-polished agate appeared on the cover of the January 1965 issue of *Lapidary Journal*. (Photograph used with permission from *Lapidary Journal Jewelry Artist*, www.jewelryartistmagazine.com.)

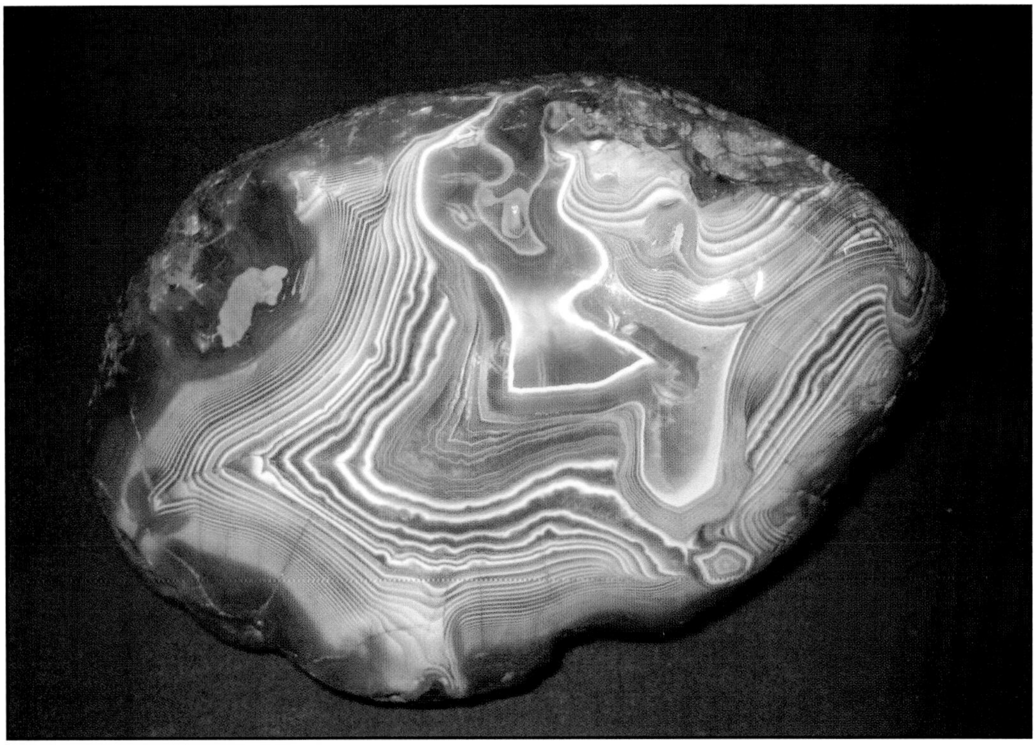

The *sixth* best polished agate weighs 2.65 pounds and was face-polished by Maynard Green after he acquired it from a farmer near Little Falls, Minnesota, in the 1970s.

This 2.27-pound classic red-and-white specimen, voted the number *five* polished Laker, showed nothing of its inner beauty prior to being cut. After agonizing for weeks, I got lucky and hit a "Home Run" after deciding to cut and polish it.

The *fourth* best Laker weighs 1.25 pounds and has rich dark colors, with a large, flawless face.

This 3.25-pound strikingly bold agate with bright white-and-red banding was voted the *third* best polished Laker.

The strikingly beautiful 2.24-pound stone called "Peanut Butter and Jelly" was voted the number *two* polished Laker. The agate was found by Peter Kraminski in beach gravel along the shore of Lake Superior, just north of Two Harbors, Minnesota. Its amazing color scheme and fracture-free polished face makes this specimen one of the most popular and rare Lake Superior agates ever.

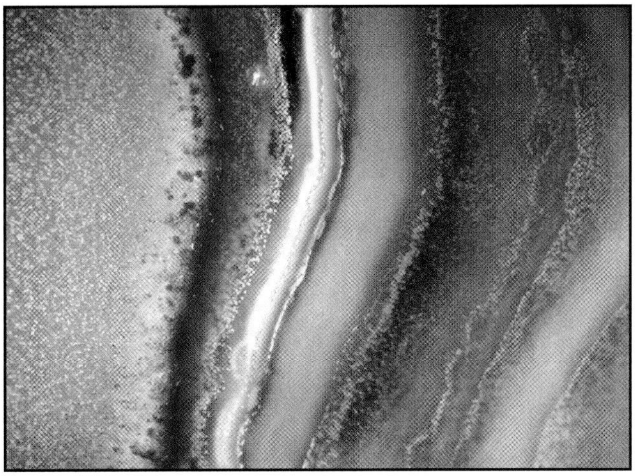

This microscopic photo shows that the amazing array of color in the Peanut Butter and Jelly agate is produced by tiny flecks of various forms of iron oxide (35X).

The number *one* polished Lake Superior agate is a classic beauty that I first saw in the Beaver Bay Agate Shop in 1987. It has all the qualities of a fantastic polished stone: shape, color, contrast, symmetry in the pattern, and a beautiful, dome-polished face.

The 0.96-pound "Perfect Pounder" was somehow left off the Top Ten Polished Laker list, but it is a true classic, with a striking concentric, red-and-white pattern. The agate was found by Robert Schussler in Lakeland, Minnesota, in July of 1979.

their insatiable appetite. I've spent some time in the northern Minnesota swamps as a budding geologist and been through more than my share of bug repellant. I had a harder time relating to the intense work it took to retrieve the precious gems. He remembered working with hammers and chisels, often in a wetsuit, trying to free the agates from their reluctant host rock. They split open boulders and the bedrock itself, often under a few feet of water. He remembered one beautiful agate in particular that he worked on for two days that was in two feet of water. They made a fire on the beach where he could keep himself warm when the numbing cold made it impossible to hold the hammer. I shuttered in my chair just thinking about it. Finally, he had to move on to a different one. The agate won out that time.

Their stories were fascinating and it was obvious that those trips to that remote agate paradise were treasured family memories. I could see the sadness in their eyes as they looked at the shelves of agates. I know that look all too well, for Clayton Sr. died within a year of my dad's death. The leader of their expeditions was no longer with them; but even I could feel his presence as I looked around the room.

I couldn't help myself in wanting to try to buy a specimen or two. But after I thought about all they went through to get these specimens, I couldn't even bring myself to ask.

As I drove back home, my mind wandered between the room full of agates and their birthplace on the island. I thought about the great glaciers that plucked the banded gemstones from within the lavas and deposited them over a vast area. From Kansas to the shores of Lake Superior, the glacial drift is speckled with agates. It is within these surficial deposits that Lakers have been and will continue to be found. However, the experience of seeing these agates from such a remote place made another thought enter my head. I couldn't help but wonder treasures lay quietly beneath the frigid swells at the bottom of Lake Superior.

It's only fitting that I let Clayton Sr., tell the tale himself of his family's experiences. The following article was written by Mr. Braun in 1976 and shares the experience, in his own words, of a unique Lake Superior agate adventure.

> Michipicoten – it's meaning in Indian is *"The land of the big bluffs"*. It is the land of the large beautiful Lake Superior agate; the wonderful people living there; stormy (and at times mirror calm) Lake Superior Indian legions; [and] past history, etc. We could go on and on.
>
> We read that Michipicoten Island was one of the few places Lake Superior agates could be found in place and being rock hounds for a number of years, scrounging road cuts, gravel pits, creek beds, mine dumps – we wanted a chance to find that BIG ONE!
>
> Our first attempt to visit the Island was met with disappointment. We couldn't seem to get any information about it. We continued on around the lake looking for agate and amethyst along the way.
>
> The next summer my wife and I and our family, Jeanne, Gary, and David, chartered a fishing boat at Michipicoten harbor, loaded all our camping gear and what we thought was enough food and took off.
>
> Of course, no one knew we were coming, but any ship entering Quebec Harbor gets a welcome by the folks living there. Mr. Gordon Dawson, the lighthouse keeper, gave us permission to camp near his home and kindly offered his services if needed.

We made arrangements to have him take us to the Junction, an area west of the harbor where we might find agates, but chances of finding any were slim. The area had been picked over so many times. Further discussion brought out the fact that there were old abandoned copper mines on the North Shore. An overgrown road across the island with several canoe portages could get us there. These mines were in operation in the early 1900s, operating only a few years, closing down and leaving all equipment behind. A large crushing wheel and steam boilers are still there.

Foolhardy and eager to explore after hearing the history of the mines from Mr. Dawson, we made plans to have him take us by boat to the Junction where we were to intercept the road crossing the island. It was to be a two-day trip with mountain, maple, and ground hemlock windfalls in abundance and all the mosquitoes on the island under the canoe with me. The first portage was about three miles which brought us all the way across. The next about one-fourth mile took us to the largest lake. We camped here overnight and started out early the next morning for the mines over a much easier road. The June berries we found were a real treat too.

We found a few minerals, small nodules of copper, some thomsonite, and inspected the ruins. Mr. Dawson was to pick us up at 7:30 p.m. and we had a long trip ahead, so we cut short our exploring, promising ourselves to come back again (but not across the island).

Eight rough miles back, we arrived in plenty of time but completely exhausted. I wouldn't recommend carrying a 78-pound canoe in the brush to anyone.

This summer we walked to the first lake and wondered how we ever managed with the canoe and camp gear. We were a little older; a little wiser.

Upon arriving back, we were surprised to find that other rock hounds had scoured the area since we had been there. Everyone but David and I had had it – we were looking along the water's edge, checking basalt lava when David called, *"Dad come here."* This is common in our family as we often check on flowers, shrubs, insects, anything to do with nature. Thus began our incredible discovery of the large agates! After much chiseling we were rewarded with a beautiful red, white, black and gray banded agate which weighed 1 1/2 pounds of top quality. You can imagine how we felt. This brought everyone into action but Mr. Dawson arrived to take us back to camp.

We wanted to go back the next day, but Lake Superior had other ideas. The next day was calmer, so back to the Junction we went. The first agate I found was a thirty pound blue, gray and white agate. We also found another that weighed 11 pounds and several in the 3 to 5 pound class. Gary found a cluster of amethyst crystals in the center. We also found many quartz geodes, and a few nice amethyst geodes, the largest weighing around 300 pounds.

We have spent our last year's vacations in Michipicoten Island and each time the two weeks just whizzed by.

Our largest agate is red carnelian with stalactites of copper showing calcite crystals shot through the center. The bottom part is a breccia type of agate. The complete agate weighs

75 pounds. Another weighs 38 pounds, that we have never cut. A chip off the front shows it to be a red carnelian with very fine bandings – top gem quality.

Practically all the agates have cracks in them, due to the type of basalt they are found in and because of the harsh elements. Large agate such as we found are available to the lucky persons who are fortunate enough to stumble across them, but they are very rare.

Today there is much prospecting for copper being done on the island. I hope that if it is economically feasible to mine copper on the island that steps will be taken to preserve its natural beauty. The island is 18 1/2 miles long and about 8 miles wide. It is very mountainous, with about 40 inland lakes. Most of the lakes have fish in them, but are very difficult to get to. There are few trails, very dense vegetation. The lower elevations have a more or less rain forest type vegetation, while some of the mountain tops have a type of tundra such as sound in the Arctic.

Very beautiful minute flowers grow on the rocks along the waters edge. At the edge of gravel bars, multi-hued wild vetch grows in profusion. In the lower areas and along the creeks many of the same flowers we have at home are giants here. Swampy areas have the beautiful moccasin flowers.

The only wild life on the island are beaver, fox, rabbits, weasel, mice and a few mink! Just like all of the North Country, you have the black flies in season and also mosquitoes. In June, the lake trout fishing is excellent and the possibilities of getting a large rainbow are good. In August, brook trout or coasters start toward the mouth of small creeks and I have seen some up to 2 feet long. Large northern pike also may be caught in the weedy bays.

If you like the out of doors, love nature in general, hope to find that big agate and like tenting and roughing it, Michipicoten is the place to go, but please leave it as clean and unspoiled as it is.

Since the writing of this article, Michipicoten is now a provincial park.

In 1985, Michipicoten Island was established as a provincial park in Canada. Lake Superior agates can no longer be removed by collectors. However, the beauty of the island and the chance to see large Lakers in their host rock (if you can find them!) would still present a memorable and exciting trip.

Frigid waves splash a huge agate nodule as it slowly erodes from its host basalt lava flow. This nearly five-foot-long nodule, almost too big to be collected, stands guard along the shore of this agate island paradise. (Photo courtesy of Alice Braun)

Essay: The *Cash and Treasures* Show

One of the benefits of the agate books I've written is that the added notoriety has presented me with many fun opportunities that wouldn't otherwise have happened. One recent opportunity came when I received a call from the Travel Channel. Mercedes Johnson, the program coordinator, asked if I would be the guide for an agate-hunting episode of their show, *Cash and Treasures*. When I learned the premise of the show, I became excited at the prospect of not only having a lot of fun, but also promoting the hobby.

It didn't take long to come up with ideas and, eventually, we agreed to go agate collecting in a farm field, a gravel pit, and scuba diving in Lake Superior, in the Upper Peninsula of Michigan. I was also excited that we would be able to get many of my fellow agate collectors, family, and friends involved in the show. I chuckled to myself when Mercedes said, *"We'd love it if you had people involved who were interesting characters."* If there's one thing we have in this hobby, it's plenty of characters!

By July of 2007, it had been eight years since I'd started scuba diving again. Copper Harbor residents George Twardzik and Jake Anderson had coaxed me into the frigid waters of Lake Superior in the summer of 2000. It was just like riding a bike after a long absence. I didn't take seventeen years off from the hobby after my Dad died while scuba diving in Australia because I was afraid to get in the water; I had just lost my enthusiasm. When Jake and George got me back into the water and I saw big, beautiful, Lake Superior agates in the bedrock on the bottom, my fire for scuba diving was rekindled. For each of the last eight summers, the three of us spend days together in Lake Superior, diving for agates. I thought people watching the show would enjoy this exciting way to look for Lakers.

After meeting the film crew for dinner at the Mariner Restaurant in Copper Harbor the night before, we loaded the scuba gear and filming equipment aboard the 43-foot-long boat *Equinox* and headed out across the harbor and into Lake Superior. The forecast was for moderate winds, with possible storms. Once away from the protection of the harbor, a light rain lashed our faces, and the boat began heaving in the growing swells kicked up by the steadily increasing winds. Our animated group quickly got to know each other and optimistically made plans for finding many great agates on the underwater gravel bar once we reached our dive spot.

As fate would have it, however, the weather only got worse. Stacy Waters, the producer of the show, got motion sickness and had to lean over the side of the boat several times during the day. In spite of the obvious misery she was in, she fought through the nausea and still did a great job. Once anchored over the underwater gravel reef, Kirsten, cameraman Stephen Buckingham, and I got suited up. By now, the wind was howling, and the water was churning. Steve jumped in first to film Kirsten and me entering the water. Just as we let go of the boat for a backwards entry, a wave lurched the boat up, and I fell about five feet into the water, flat on my back. The unexpected jolt got my immediate attention, but it was the unexpected strong current that raised my alarm. Within seconds, the three of us were being carried away from the reef into deeper water. We all struggled against the current and the waves, trying to get back to the boat.

After what seemed like an eternity, we each climbed out of the water onto the rollicking platform. I then looked at both Kirsten and Stacy and said, *"It isn't going to happen today; it's too dangerous."* Jake and George had followed us in Jake's boat, and George popped his head out of the water, just as we started removing our gear. With wide eyes he said, *"That was the hardest swim I've ever had out here."* He agreed that we needed to head back to the harbor, but along the way over to us, he found a couple of agates on the reef. George reached into his nylon bag and pulled out a solid, beautifully fine-banded, 3/4-pound agate.

An hour later, as we anchored on the east end of Copper Harbor, the wind died down, and the sun came out. Kirsten, Steve, and I suited up again and, as we jumped in for a second time, a bank of thick, dark clouds quickly moved in from the west. The second storm packed more high winds and kicked up 3- to 4-foot swells *inside* the harbor! The three of us were already underwater and kept right on swimming, as large raindrops began pounding the surface of the water above us. We had a great time finding small agates in 10- to 15-feet deep water, wondering if Stacy was bending over the side above us, yet again.

The second storm moved through quickly and just as we pulled up the anchor, the sun came out once again. As we made our way back to the dock, the wind was still howling, and in spite of all she'd been through, Stacy was happy with the footage they were able to get. In spite of the challenging conditions, we still found several nice, smaller-sized agates. Most importantly, everyone was safe.

The host of the Travel Channel's *Cash and Treasures* show, Kirsten Gum, recreates a scene from the movie *Titanic* on the bow of the "Equinox" in Copper Harbor in Michigan, July 10, 2007. It was an especially challenging day scuba diving for Lake Superior agates, with high winds, large swells, driving rain, and strong currents.

The following morning, George Twardzik and I piled into my truck and we led the film crew in their two vehicles on an eight-hour trek south through the Upper Peninsula of Michigan, west across northern Wisconsin, and eventually into central Minnesota, near the town of Little Falls. At around 3:00 p.m., our caravan arrived at an 80-acre farm field, where we had previously arranged permission to pick agates. Already waiting for us were several of the "agate boys," including Bruce Peddle, Jim Rodeski, Dave Ringwelski and his son, Taylor. We introduced the film crew to our friends who gave Kirsten a few pointers on finding agates in farm fields. The field had been recently turned over, and glacial rocks of all sizes were scattered everywhere. I then explained to Kirsten that the best thing about this field was there were no footprints! It was a virgin field, with good potential for agates. Kirsten was chomping at the bit to get started, so away we went.

After taking literally a dozen steps, we found our first agate. It was about ½ pound in size, with a lot of quartz. Not a great find, but definitely a good indicator. George and I walked on either side of Kirsten, giving her pointers on what to look for. We jokingly said that if she wanted to be a true agate picker, she had to lick the dirt off the first agate she found. Ever the good sport, a few moments later, she found a ¼-pounder right between us and excitedly licked the dirt off without any hesitation. It turned out the agate was of excellent quality, with beautiful shadow effect in the banding. Nobody can accuse her or the crew of planting any agates, either. That nice one she found was caught live on camera!

On July 11, 2007, *Cash and Treasure* host, Kirsten Gum, proudly displays a beautiful ¼-pound shadow agate she found, with George Twardzik and I on each side of her, as the cameras were rolling.

Just as we were finishing up the shoot, a dark-colored thunderhead closed in on us at about 6:00 p.m. A pouring rain chased us off to our final stop of the day, a gravel pit near Milaca, Minnesota. Long-time friend Gerry Lang had graciously made arrangements for us to take the crew agate picking in an active commercial gravel pit. Janet, Grant, and Amanda met us at the pit to join in the fun. We had lots of fun, but little luck searching on the drop and low banks. However, we did find several nice specimens in the sorted rock piles. Once again, Kirsten got lucky, finding a beautiful red-and-white "Candy-stripper" in the 1½" decoration rock pile. Minutes later, Janet pulled out a ½-pounder with bright white bands that was easily the best agate of the day.

Kirsten found a beautiful red-and-white banded agate in the 1½" sorted rock pile as the sun was setting on July 11, 2007.

The next day, the film crew spent the morning at Michael Carlson's house in Minneapolis, where he face-polished the shadow agate Kirsten found the day before. Later in the day, they filmed my personal collection of Lake Superior agates, which helped give them a better perspective of what can be found, but also how difficult it is to find a really good, big one. The day ended with a barbeque on the deck of our home that gave everyone a chance to relax and recount the whirlwind events of the previous three days. The highlight of the evening was when our gymnast daughter Amanda taught Kirsten how to do a flip on our trampoline!

On Friday morning, we all made the pilgrimage to Moose Lake, Minnesota, for the annual Agate Days gem and mineral show to film the part of the show where Kirsten takes all her finds to see how much "cash" she can get for them. Unfortunately, their schedule did not allow them to stay until Saturday, when the real festivities began. However, in the hotel parking lot at the AmericInn, about a dozen dealers set up impromptu tables to sell agates a day early. It was like a "Mini-Moose Lake" show, with about 100 people milling about.

George and I introduced Kirsten to the dealers and watched as she worked her magic. At one point, I jokingly told her she wouldn't get $5 for a tiny eye agate she had found. Being a fierce competitor, she guaranteed me she could get more. Upon approaching a table with several people smiling, and the cameras rolling, Kirsten launched into her sales pitch. After singing the praises of the modest specimen she held, she then said, *"Who is going to give me $10 for this beautiful eye agate?"* Wisconsin collector Gary Richards spoke up and said, *"I'll buy it."* He then took off his glasses to reveal his missing left eye and said, *"I could use another good eye."* As the crowd roared with laughter, Gary handed her the money that Kirsten proudly waved in front of me.

The week-long experience with the film crew was absolutely wonderful. They couldn't have been more professional, polite, and fun. I'm not sure if everything went the way they wanted, but they seemed happy with the outcome.

The premier of our agate episode aired on December 11, 2007. Fellow agate collectors Charlie White and Bruce Strohschien watched the show with Janet and me, and we thought it came across very well. Everyone looked like they had a good time on the show and, judging from the feedback over the next several weeks, it was obvious that a lot of people enjoyed the program, even though we didn't find any monsters. I think everyone enjoyed the experience, and our hobby definitely received a positive shot in the arm.

The *Cash and Treasures* gang posed for a final picture at the Moose Lake Agate Days on July 13, 2007. Left to right: Mark Mostad, Stacy Waters, Steve Buckingham, Kirsten Gum, Scott and Janet Wolter, George and Lisa Twardzik, and Luke Sauer.

CHAPTER 6
Types of Agates and their Formation

Most people, when they think of agates, think of beautiful banded stones. Consequently, banded agates are the most popular and sought-after variety of the gemstone. But agates come in many different varieties, often equally beautiful, even if less well known. This chapter describes some of the more common types of Lake Superior agates and presents my interpretation of the conditions that probably existed at the time of their formation.

To understand the formation of the different types of Lake Superior agates, you should know something about chalcedony, the basic material of agates and one of the many different forms of the mineral quartz. To the naked eye and even under magnification, chalcedony appears as a very hard, massive deposit. In fact, however, it is composed of very slender, fiber-like crystals that can only be seen under an electron microscope.

On Moh's hardness scale (Figure 6-1) chalcedony, like quartz, has a hardness of 7. This is hard enough to resist ordinary wear and tear but it also makes the stones very workable as cutting and polishing material. Chalcedony and quartz differ, however, in the specific gravity and refractive index (Figure 6-2). These differences are attributable to tiny spaces, filled with water and possibly air, between the needle-like, fibrous crystals of chalcedony. Crystalline quartz has a more orderly arrangement, with molecules packed so tightly that no air or water-filled voids exist.

MOH'S HARDNESS SCALE

HARDNESS NUMBER	MINERAL
1	Talc
2	Gypsum
3	Calcite
4	Fluorite
5	Apatite
6	Feldspar
7	Quartz
8	Topaz
9	Corundum
10	Diamond

Figure 6-1

Because natural quartz occurs in these two different types, the conditions under which they form must differ. Laboratory studies show that both the pressure and temperature of silica in solution differs during the formation of chalcedony and quartz. Chalcedony forms near the surface under relatively low pressure at temperatures between 100 to 3000 degrees Celsius. Quartz forms under pressure ranging from atmospheric (one bar or 14.7 pounds per square inch) to 19 kilobars, and crystallizes at 573 degrees Celsius in the surface environment.

PHYSICAL PROPERTIES

		Quartz	Chalcedony
Hardness	(Moh's Hardness)	7	7
Refractive Index		1.544-1.553	1.533-1.539
Specific Gravity		2.651	2.58-2.64
Temperature	(Celsius)	573 degrees	100-300 degrees
Pressure	(Kilobars)	0-19	0-5

Figure 6-2

Since both quartz and chalcedony occur within North Shore lava flows, variable temperature and pressure conditions must have existed during the Precambrian rifting event that formed them. Cyclic, pulsating volcanism originating from deep within the earth produced the variability in temperature and silica solution level within the rift valley system. The depth at which crystallization occurred most directly affected pressure.

The easily recognized banded or **fortification agate** makes a good starting point for discussion of agate types. The term "fortification" is used because the enclosing structure of each exposed band pattern is similar to the enclosing walls of an old-time fort. As noted earlier, banding becomes exposed through abrasion during and after glacial transport, producing an endless variety of fortification patterns. These banding patterns are so distinctive, that like snowflakes and human beings, no two agates are exactly the same.

Although this basic classification includes all agates with continuous banding patterns that can be traced on exposed surfaces, many classifications of banding patterns and types exist. Certain agates have similar, unmistakable characteristics and probably originated within the same flow or from solutions with similar composition. In fact, I've seen many examples over the years of similar agates occurring within lava flows peppered with agates while diving in Lake Superior and exposed along the North and South shores. Color is the primary feature used in grouping many agates. The following varieties are only a sampling of the many different types of fortification agates.

The banding on **painted agates** or **paint-stones** appears as a series of zones of deep color that look as though they had been painted with a brush. The colors are primarily deep reds and oranges with white banding, but blues and greens and occasionally yellow are also seen. The painted appearance is caused by heavy initial concentrations of dissolved minerals within the chalcedony, combined with subsequent heavy oxidation (see Portfolio, pages C7 and C8).

The very distinctive and beautiful painted agates called **Paradise Beach agates** are named for the North Shore beach near Grand Marais, Minnesota, where the lava flows containing them are found. They are most often orange, and are distinguished from other paint-stones by the presence of native copper within the amygdules. Cut samples often reveal fine stringers of copper, with the husks and weathered surfaces of the host basalt lavas often containing copper oxides.

Gray or **black agates** are very common and characteristically display very fine to faint banding. Their general absence of color is due to low concentrations of iron ions and iron oxides. Long or intense exposure to oxidation will bring out some red or yellow color.

Bleached agates are thought to have been exposed to long periods of sunlight and weathering. Some specimens show a lighter color, usually white, on only one side of the stone. The color contact marks the boundary between the exposed and shielded surfaces. These agates are exceedingly rare, perhaps because very few agates spent prolonged periods at the surface.

An agate with a complete fortification pattern throughout it is said to be "solid." Sometimes, however, the silica-rich solutions stopped flowing before an agate was completed. Such an incompletely filled agate with a void-space, or hole, remaining is called a **geode agate**. Geode agates are usually lined with quartz crystals that protrude into the cavity. Often, these crystals are transparent, with well developed faces, but two other geode crystal varieties also exist. Dark quartz crystals that appear black are called *smoky quartz*. The dark brown to black variety, which is probably caused by exposure to natural radioactivity, is very rare. More common within geode agates are the beautiful violet *amethyst crystals*. Trace amounts of ferric iron (Fe^{+++}) give amethyst its lavender color.

One variety of Laker with crystalline quartz, that often produces attractive specimens, is called a **"floater".** These agates are produced when alternating layers of chalcedony bands appear to float between the transparent quartz crystal layers.

This spectacular 2.65-pound agate with alternating bands of white agate and clear quartz is called a "floater".

A slightly less common variety of banded agate is the **parallel-banded** or **water level agate**. The water-level agate has many of the same colors and features as fortification agates. During its formation, however, the solutions were not under hydrostatic or flooded-cavity pressure. Solutions entered and filled the cavity, then drained out leaving a small puddle that crystallized into a straight or parallel band of chalcedony. Each parallel band can be traced continuing on up and over the "roof" of the vesicle. Subsequent un-pressurized solutions deposited more parallel bands until the vesicle filled completely or fluid pressure returned and a fortification pattern completed the top of the agate. An interesting feature of the water-level agate is that it allows determination of the top and bottom of the agate and how it was positioned while still in the lava flow. In contrast, the relative position within the flow of a complete fortification agate can only be guessed at.

Coined "mosaic" agate, this polygonal pattern found at the bottom of some water-level agates was probably produced by drying shrinkage cracking of the first horizontal band deposited. This pattern resembles a mud puddle after drying in the sun. Subsequent horizontal layers of agate deposited over the first cracked band fill the open cracks with silica much like a "ruin" agate.

The **moss agate** is probably the least appreciated variety of the gemstone. It was formed by the presence of dendritic, moss-like, aggregates of material that either crystallized inside the vesicle before solutions entered or were carried in with the solutions. Analysis of the moss material reveals that it is composed primarily of iron oxide or manganese oxide. Because this material was present when the chalcedony formed, the characteristic bands are usually not well developed. The solutions crystallized into massive chalcedony during a single prolonged flooding of the vesicle, trapping the solid oxide minerals in a quartz tomb. Cut and polished moss agates have a beauty all their own. With a little imagination, that trapped oxide minerals can often be seen to resemble figures and landscapes.

The **tube agate** is another rare and very beautiful variety. The tubes were formed by hair-thin projections of rod-like minerals, usually vertical and parallel to one another. As the chalcedony began to crystallize around these obstructions, the banding followed the contours of the projections, creating beautiful patterns. Tubes encircled by massive clear quartz are common; when the quartz is polished, the tubes are beautifully displayed. Tubes within agates vary in diameter and length from 1 millimeter to more than 2 inches in a few large specimens.

Good examples of **ruin agates** are extremely rare. They were formed while the agates were still trapped within the lava flow. Tremors from earthquakes associated with volcanism cracked and faulted many of the flows and the agates within them. The cracks disfiguring the agates were subsequently cemented back together by later solutions of chalcedony. In most specimens, displaced banding can be seen, and the intensity of the tremor may be related to the thickness of the re-cemented fracture and the amount of displacement or offset of the bands.

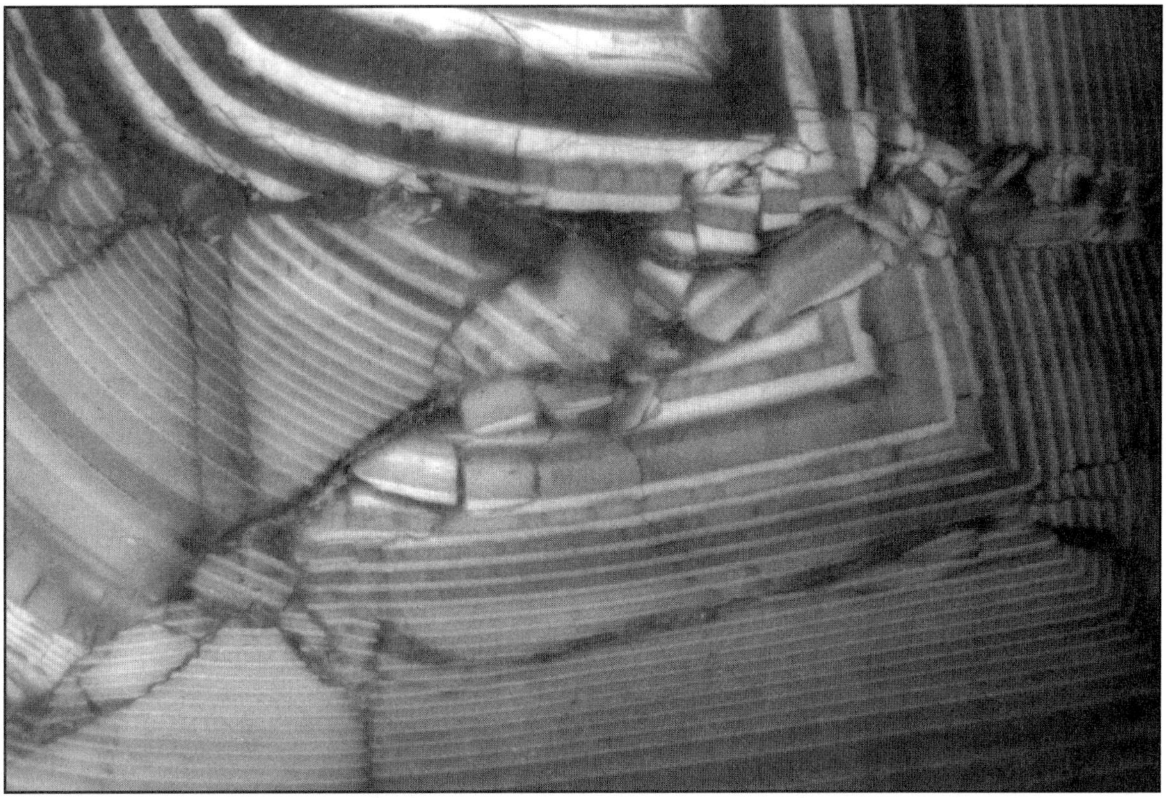

Faulting which occurred when the agate was still trapped in its host lava flow, produced tiny angular pieces along the fracture. Later silica solutions sealed the fracture entombing the broken shards of agate producing what is called a "ruin" agate (10X).

The **eye agate** is undoubtedly the most popular variety, perhaps because the perfectly round shape really does look like an eye staring back at the viewer. It is also the hardest variety to find, however, and it may be the agate whose formation is most mysterious and controversial. The nucleated gel theory seems to answer many questions about the eye agate's origin. The theory states that as solutions entered the vacant vesicle, their consistency was that of "runny" gelatin. When the solution level dropped, and the vesicle was drained of most of the gel, the remaining gel began to form perfectly round droplets, or "bead up" on the inside of the vesicle wall. This beading up of the gelatin solution was probably caused by nucleation around certain points, of the individual chalcedony needles. Subsequently, the droplet crystallized into solid chalcedony "eyes." Later, more fluid solutions deposited concentric fortification bands around the eyes. The fact that all eyes within a given agate have the same overall appearance and color supports the idea of a single gelatin thick solution. Occasionally the resulting shapes are tightly clustered into groups resembling a bunch of grapes. This unusual feature in agates is called *"botryoidal texture."*

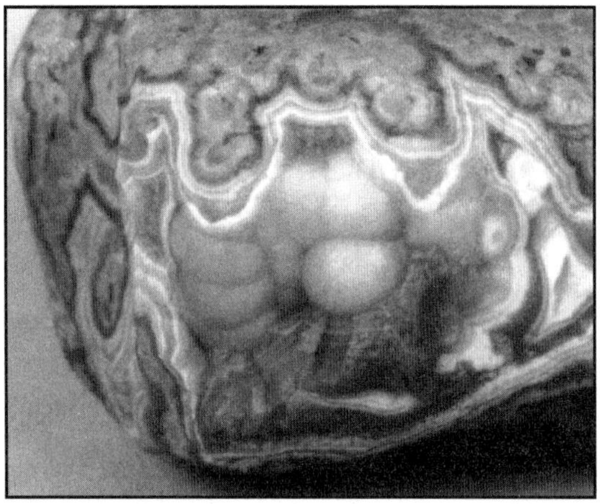

Clusters of sphere shaped chalcedony that resembles a bunch of grapes are called botryoidal texture.

An eye agate's value is determined by the number and size of the eyes. Single agates with as many as 50 small (less then 1 millimeter) eyes have been found. The largest single eye known to the author is one measuring 2 1/2" in diameter (see Portfolio, page C17).

Another very special type of Laker is called **sagenite agate**. Sagenite agate is a variety that contains needle-shaped mineral inclusions that typically form radiating "bushes" or "sprays." The orderly arranged spray originates from a central point with well defined, straight crystals. The crystals are composed of rutile, goethite or both. The color of the sagenite crystals vary from jet black to a golden copper.

Sagenite can be found as a microscopic-sized spray between banding, or as several bushes, or even one massive bush which fills the entire nodule. Many specimens with sagenite are banded with beautiful color. Rarely are rough sagenite agates that impressive. However, polished specimens can be quite beautiful, especially cut through the center of the spray. A with all types of Lake Superior agates, magnification reveals a whole new world of complexity and beauty. This is certainly true with sagenite agates.

This spectacular, finely banded polished sagenite agate has an amazing 360 degree spray of rutile needles. The 0.32-pound specimen was originally found in Duluth, Minnesota.

There is a variety of Lake Superior agate that burst on the scene in the latter part of the 1990s called **Blue or "Skip-an-atom" agate.** These agates have a unique and distinct light bluish-gray color with fibrous-like crystalline quartz that is often bright white in color. Examples of skip-an-atom agate occur as fortification, water-level, tube, and moss varieties. Although the author has not personally seen a skip-an-atom eye agate example, I'm quite sure they exist. Ted Vanasse wrote about these agates in his book giving credit for their description by Ludwig A. Koelnau in the September, 1940, *Mineralogist.* Though the name implies something about the mode of formation, the reason for the lavender blue coloration is *"...due simply to a diluted combination of bluish-white chalcedony and hematite."* (Vanansse, 1958, page 50) Reports from collectors suggest specific lava flows occur along the North Shore that contains examples of up to over twenty pounds in size.

Essay: The Basement Full of Agates

Every now and then die-hard agate enthusiasts dream about agates. I certainly have, and I have heard other collectors confess that visions of the banded gemstone have interrupted their otherwise peaceful slumbers. Then most common dreams are of finding a large, beautiful specimen or stumbling onto an area where nearly every rock is an agate. Sometimes a particular agate will continually recur in a collector's dreams. Occasionally, there are nightmares of a favorite stone being lost or destroyed.

Moat of us acknowledge that dreams, good or bad, rarely come true. About 22 years ago, however, a dream of mine became a reality. I still find it hard to believe what I experienced on that cold, rainy night.

My real-life dream began in the spring of 1985, when someone told me about a fellow named Maynard Green. He was reputed to have a very nice agate collection, including a beautiful 6-pound, red-and-white agate. Excited at the prospect of photographing such a large and beautiful specimen (and perhaps others), I set out to find him. I first met Maynard at the St. Paul gem and Mineral Show that summer. I went there, initially to pick up my then girlfriend Janet's engagement ring from a gemologist friend who was selling material at the show. I brought three 2-pound agates along as collateral for the ring until my next paycheck, since I wanted the ring in time to propose marriage on the fifth anniversary of our first date. I also wanted to show Maynard some of my agates to let him know I was a serious collector.

I asked his whereabouts, and before long he was pointed out to me. Soon we were talking up a storm. He was a delightful person, and before we parted he invited me to visit him in his small hometown of Grand meadow, Minnesota, near the Iowa border. After all I had heard about Maynard's collection, both from him and others, I couldn't wait to get there.

Within a couple of weeks, I had called Maynard and made plans for a visit, and soon my new fiancée and I showed up at Maynard's door. He and his wife, Amy, welcomed us into their home to show us Maynard's agates. The first display we saw was a large case with several dozen polished agates ranging in size up to half a pound. Although they were beautiful, we wanted to see bigger rocks, so Maynard directed us to a corner case containing large face-polished agates, some weighing as much as 3 pounds. A few were absolutely great, but, pretty as they were I was disappointed that he didn't have any big rough stones. Fortunately, I was to be pleasantly surprised.

After we had admired his polished specimens, Maynard led us into another room containing a glass case with dimensions of six feet by three feet by two feet. When he turned on the light, my eyes opened wide in amazement. The case was filled with large, rough perfect agates. I couldn't believe it! He had about 100 agates weighing a pound or more. It would take ten lifetimes of constant searching to find that many beautiful gemstones. I immediately spotted the 6-pounder I had heard so much about, and it was a beauty, with thick, perfect, alternating red-and-white bands. I could understand what everyone was talking about (see Portfolio, Page C6). As I scanned the rocks, however, my attention focused on a 2 1/2 pound specimen with an unbelievable banded face. Someday, I resolved silently, I would have to try to buy or trade for it, but now was not the time.

I had brought a red, white, and blue agate as well as my prize 5 3/4-pounder along for to Maynard to see, and he asked why they looked so good. I realized that none of Maynard's agates were treated; every one was still in the rough. I knew I had to enlighten him. I asked if I could demonstrate the procedure on one of his untreated agates and he said, *"Be my guest."* I then lifted the 2 1/2 pound agate I liked out of the case and went to work. After I had oiled it up, he seemed genuinely impressed.

Maynard Green posed outside his home holding the 2.65-pound polished beauty (see Portfolio page C29) during my visit in the spring of 1985.

When Maynard led me into the basement, another astonishing sight met my eyes. Boxes, bags, sacks, trays, and every sort of container you could imagine, all full of Lake Superior agates. I was in total shock. The whole basement was a treasure chest of stone he had collected over the last 30 years from people who saved their agates for him. He explained that every year he made several trips around the state to buy agates. No wonder he has such a great collection! Then he took me behind the stairway, where a mound of gunny sacks lay, and said, *"The next time you come down we'll go through those rocks."* Years ago, he later explained, the first thing he did when he returned from his statewide buying trips was to put the agates through a screening sieve one-and-a-half inches in diameter. The larger agates that did not pass through the sieve he put into the sacks. My mouth watered at the prospect of sorting through those sacks, and I let Maynard know it.

He then asked me if would be interested in displaying my collection at the Austin Gem and Mineral show coming up in two months. Naturally, I said I would be honored, and he offered to let me stay at their house. As Janet and I drove back to Minneapolis, I couldn't stop thinking about the treasures in those sacks and what I would offer him for the agate I wanted most.

The weekend of the show finally arrived and as I headed back to Austin with my car packed with agates, my excitement and anticipation were building. I reached the fairgrounds at dusk and found Maynard and the other dealers setting up their displays. I quickly unpacked my rocks and put them into the glass case he had reserved for me. Then he, Amy, and I climbed into his truck for the 20-mile trek to Grand Meadow.

When we arrived, we again viewed his case, but now the stones had been cleaned and treated with mineral oil and what a difference it made! He had obviously been impressed by what I had shown him, and it made me feel great. I spotted my favorite agate, and it looked even better than I remembered. We examined and discussed agates until 2 a.m. Although the day of the show would be a long one, Maynard promised that we would look through the sacks under the basement stairs when we returned. I could hardly wait.

It was 8:00 p.m. before we arrived back at Maynard's but despite the long day and the temptations of a televised Minnesota-Oklahoma college football game, it didn't take much coaxing from Maynard to get me to join him in the basement. As we climbed down the stairs, I couldn't help but wonder what prizes were waiting in those sacks. Many hadn't been looked at in over 25 years. My heart pounded with excitement. Maynard grabbed a large plastic tub, into which we dumped about 40 pounds of dusty, dirty agates from on of the sacks. Together we carried the tub to a corner of the basement, where there was a sink with a garden hose attached to the faucet. Maynard sprayed the dust and dirt off to expose a tub of large, glittering, banded gemstones.

We then started sorting through the stones, pulling the highest quality agates out and placing them into an even larger tub. These would be cleaned, treated, and either added to Maynard's collection or sold. The agates ranged in size from 1/2 pound to 3 pounds or more. We started sorting slowly but quickened our pace when we realized how many sacks we wanted to sort through. After we had selected the best rocks from each tub, we put the rest back into the sack, I would then grab another sack and away we'd go again: wash, sort, and re-sack.

Each time we sprayed water on a tub of agates, a rush of excitement shot through me as the dust and dirt washed away. It seemed unreal to see so many beautiful agates all at once. I realized how spoiled I was becoming when I thought about all the hours I spend and miles I cover searching for just one or two really nice stones. Occasionally, I caught myself giggling or gasping in disbelief. I laughed to myself when I thought that no one would believe me when I told this story.

Four hours, 25 to 30 sacks and several hundred pounds of agates later, we emptied the last sack. My arms ached from lifting the tub, sacks and agates. When we finished, it was after midnight again, and the larger tub was filled with 200 to 300 beautiful, high-grade agates. I stared at them in disbelief; Maynard simply seemed pleased that the job was done. He thanked me and I thanked him. We then headed back up the stairs for a well-deserved break.

We sat down on the couch and Maynard poured each of us a glass of his special high-powered cherry liqueur. We leaned back, toasted our hobby in general along with that evening's efforts in particular, and took a swallow. The drink had quite a bite, but it tasted good. I thought that perhaps this was the time to make a bid for the agate I wanted.

Gingerly, I mentioned that I wanted to buy an agate in his case. He immediately smiled, knowing which one I meant. He asked what I thought would be a fair exchange. I produced two polished specimens I had brought along, a beautiful 1 1/4-pounder and a 3/4-pounder. I then laid $150 on the table next to the agates and held my breath. Maynard responded, *"Let's go take a look at it"*, and led me to the case. I pulled out the agate and made my last pitch. Maynard seemed a little sad, and I took this to be his way of saying he wanted to keep the stone. I could understand this because no amount of money would make me part with one of my best agates. I returned the agate to the case, disappointed, but glad that I had at least made the offer. We talked a few minutes about some other beauties and suddenly Maynard looked first at me, than at the agate in the case and said, *"You'd better take it out and take it home with you."* I couldn't believe it! Although I felt a little guilty, I was delighted to get such a beautiful stone (see Portfolio, page C6).

We sat down at the kitchen table and Maynard poured us another drink. He picked up the agate, gently kissed it good-bye, and put it into my hands. Sincerely moved, all I could do was say *"Thank you."* The man is as much a gem as the agate he passed onto me.

I took another sip of my drink and, as I felt its relaxing effect, my thoughts drifted back to the basement and what I had just experienced. I realized that I might be the only person ever to live out the dream of every Lake Superior agate collector.

CHAPTER 7
Microscopic Features in Agates

Although most people enjoy the striking beauty of Lake Superior agates, few are familiar with any feature except the most prominent: banding. Even those collectors who are familiar with some of the distinguishing characteristics used to help locate agates in the field may not know how these features originated. This chapter describes some of the many varied features of agates and presents some theories about their origin.

Fill Hole

The fill hole is the point at which solutions first entered the vesicle or cavity in which the agate formed. When examining a sufficiently exposed agate, you can see how banding "pinches in" and becomes tighter near the fill hole and how it radiates away from that point. Often, two or more fill holes are present, one of which will be recognized as the spot where most of the fluid movement occurred. Clear quartz will generally mark the fill hole during the final phase of silica deposition. As a rule, clear quartz at the fill hole or anywhere else in an agate is undesirable, but in some specimens a small "belly-button" of clear quartz actually enhances an agate's beauty.

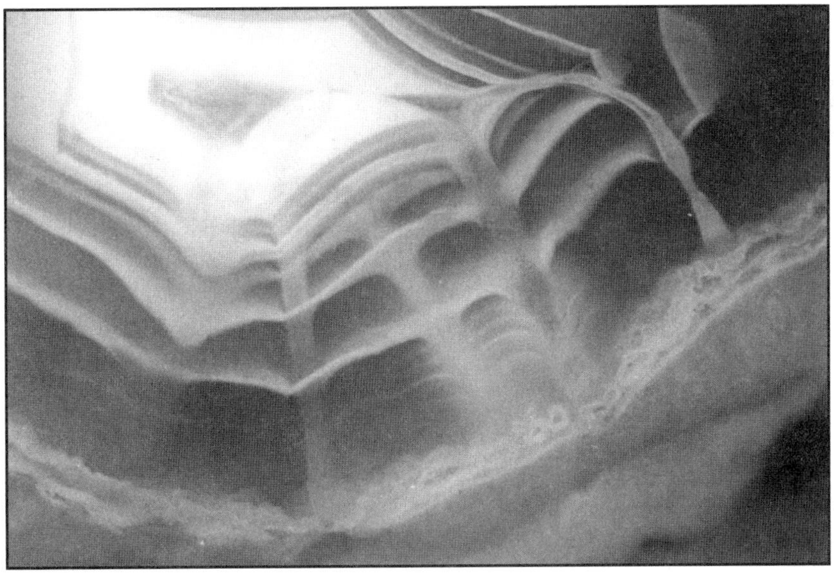

At least four obvious fill holes appear to penetrate banding layers eventually reaching the exterior surface of the agate. The bright white fortification center pattern almost looks like an angular heart in the stone with chalcedony filled arteries coursing through the body of the agate (10X).

Pinch and Swell Banding

The varying thickness of the banding is easily visible in nearly all agates. Rarely will a continuous band maintain a uniform thickness throughout. Many agates exhibit banding that narrows and is sometimes completely cut off. This pinching-off of bands usually occurs near the fill hole.

One theory about this feature is that the current velocity of solutions entering and leaving the vesicle is fastest at the fill hole. The faster current flow associated with this relatively small area carried away the fine-grained chalcedony and accessory iron oxides from the depositional surface. Pinched-off bands within the vesicle were probably caused by eddy currents similar to those seen in rivers. These high velocity flow areas prohibited uniform accumulation of chalcedony.

The pinching white bands in this agate represented an area where silica-rich solutions flowed relatively fast. During the agate's formation, chalcedony deposition was minimal because of the erosive native of faster moving solutions in that part of the vesicle. Pinching and swelling of banding thickness is directly related to the velocity of solution circulation within the vesicle (12X).

Clear Quartz

Another important feature in agates is the occurrence of white, transparent, macro-crystalline quartz. Clear quartz, often called "sugar quartz" or "crystal" is very common and not highly prized. The presence of clear quartz in an agate suggests that after a certain amount of banded chalcedony was deposited, the remaining void space in the vesicle was flooded by silica-rich solutions relatively free of accessory minerals. Examples of these crystals range from almost completely filled vesicles of quartz called "quartz balls" to the small "belly-buttons" of clear quartz at the fill holes of nearly complete banded agates.

Generally, clear quartz agates are a disappointment for the agate hunter. Often, however, the formation of clear quartz crystals stopped after a short period of growth, allowing the formation of one of three very desirable kinds of agates. When no further crystal quartz or banded chalcedony growth took place, quartz crystal tops, or terminations, protruded into the void space, producing geode agates. Geode quartz crystals are usually transparent, but black and violet varieties also occur. Good geodes agate specimens with well-developed fortification patterns are rare.

Geode agates also provide the foundation for other features in agates containing clear quartz. If chalcedony precipitated over the crystal tops within the geode, an undulating pattern called "lacy banding" developed. If the formation of new banding stopped and clear quartz was deposited a second time, the bands sandwiched between the clear quartz are called "floating bands." If fortification continued over the crystal tops to complete the agate, the second set of bands produced what is called an agate within an agate.

Alternating banded chalcedony and clear quartz zones produce very beautiful gemstones. In addition, experts can use the banding and clear quartz deposits to estimate the temperature, pressure, and solution characteristics at the time of a particular agate's formation. Thus, these features contain both beauty and clues to the agate's complex history.

Color

People often wonder what gives the Lake Superior agate its wide range of color. The red, orange, yellow, and brown colors are caused by the oxidation of iron ions, primarily ferrous iron (Fe^{++}), to form hematite. The many shades can be attributed to the carrying concentrations of iron and the amount of weathering the iron experienced. Often, different gradations of weathering can be seen on a single agate, indicating areas that were exposed for different lengths of time and intensity.

Careful examinations of agates also reveal tiny red specks or flakes of the mineral hematite. These specks are best viewed with an inexpensive hand-lens (magnification 10x), or a binocular stereomicroscope. They occur along the flat plane on the outer edge of individual bands. The amount of hematite along these band planes is directly responsible for the eventual intensity of the gemstone's bright red color, which is greatly enhanced when exposed to oxidation. In rare instances, these hematite flakes resemble the shape of a tree leaf. Without these oxidizing iron ions and hematite specks, the Lake Superior agate would lack much of the color and quality that make it such a highly prized gemstone.

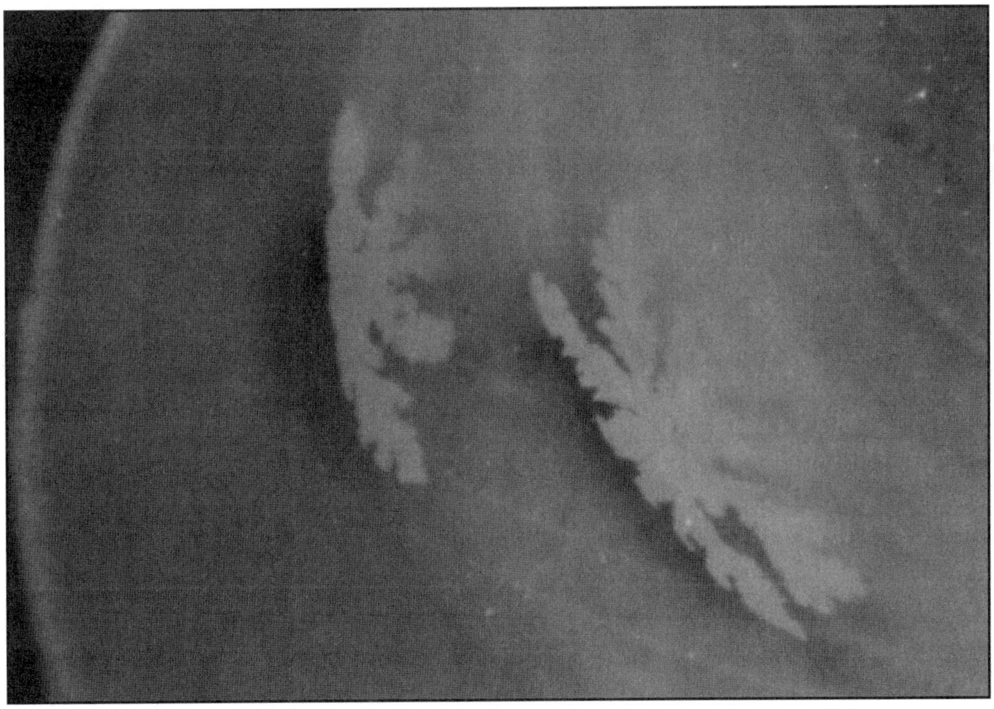

Two bright orange "maple leaves" of dendritic hematite dip gently away form the surface of the agate, following the banding plane. The hematite probably grew along the banding surfaces whenthe chalcedony was still in the fluid state. (30X)

Pits and Pockmarks

Bubble-like depressions called "pits" or "pochmarks" on the exterior husk are eye-catching features very helpful to agate hunters. These small, very common depressions vary in diameter and depth. Often, only one side or area of an agate will be pitted. Magnified examinations of individuals pits show very small (tenth of a millimeter) round craters on the pit surfaces; in other words; pitted pits, or micro-pits.

Although no one has yet provided a complex explanation for how these depressions formed, there is one theory that seems to answer a few questions. This theory is that the pits and micro-pits were caused by rounded projections or "botryoidal" masses of the minerals prehnite, calcite, and epidote that precipitated inside the vesicles before the silica-rich solutions entered and crystallized around them. Because thee minerals are softer than chalcedony, they were quickly eroded by glacial and other weathering processes.

Crystal Impressions

Another common but curious feature that occurs on the husk, leaving an imprint in the agate, is crystal impressions. These impressions consist of very distinctive flat surfaces with perfect angles, resembling crystal faces. Many of these faces appear as six-sided rhombohedrons that come to a perfect point.

These crystal impressions are composed of the mineral calcite, which crystallized and grew within the vesicle form solutions rich in calcium carbonate ($CaCO_3$). Later, warm silica-rich solutions deposited chalcedony around the calcite crystals. Calcite, however, dissolves readily in cool water, and so was washed away by rain, snow, and glacial melt-water when erosion freed the agate. The six-sided impressions record the long-vanished calcite's existence. Other types of crystal impressions seen in Lake Superior agates are the flat, tabular blades of the mineral barite ($BaSO_4$) and the cubic habit of pyrite (FeS_2).

The cubic crystal habit exhibited by the impressions on the husk of this agate was probably made by the mineral pyrite. The pyrite grew inside the vesicle prior to the formation of the agate. Subsequently, the pyrite crystals weathered quickly away during glacial transport (10X).

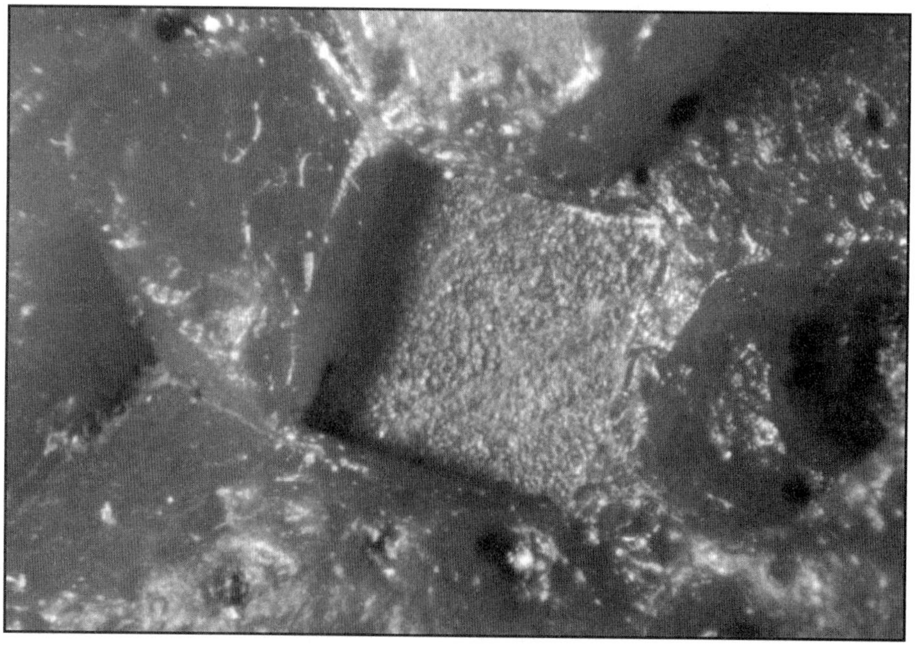

Sagenite

Sagenite is a radiating cluster of the rod-like mineral rutile that resembles a sunburst in cross-section. It is believed to have crystallized inside the vesicle from a solution rich in titanium. When chalcedony entered the vesicle, it crystallized around the saginite into both banded agate and occasionally into a massive, nonbanded deposit. Rough examples of sagenite are typically not very impressive, but cut and polished pieces are very beautiful. Large specimens are rare and highly prized.

Shadow

A feature commonly seen in agates is the eye-catching illusion of a dark line that races across the pattern of a well banded agate. This optical effect of movement within the agate is called shadow, and is caused by the eye perceiving depth in the agate. Depth is perceived because of the clear chalcedony between the opaque bands but only when the bands are perfectly parallel to each other and to the line of sight. Because the bands and turn within the agate, so does the shadow. When the agate is rotated, the shadow races along the banding and turns at corners, creating an enjoyable visual display. It was once thought that up to 10,000 bands per inch were needed to produce this effect; but using a binocular microscope to count the bands in agates displaying shadow gives an actual range between 50 and 500 bands per inch.

Shadow agates are rarely recognized in the field. Although rough stones may have the shadow potential of banding exposed, oxidation covers the clear chalcedony between bands, masking the visible shadow effect. Beautiful examples, however, can easily be obtained through cutting and polishing. Shadow agates are highly prized, and exceptional specimens have an almost mesmerizing effect on the viewer.

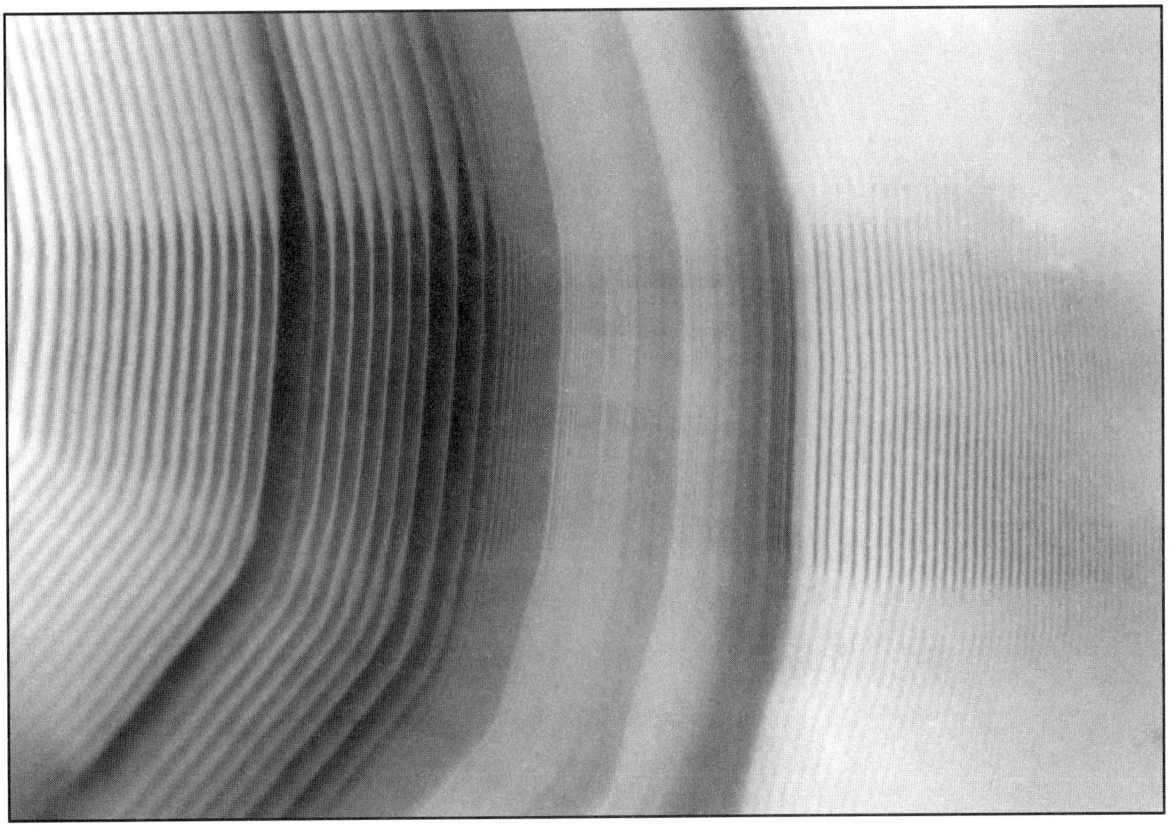

Shadow effect in agates is produced when the banding is aligned parallel to the viewer's eye so that depth is perceived into the stone. This pleasing optic effect can often be seen racing across the face of a finely banded specimen as it is turned (16X).

SHADOW AGATE BANDING COUNT
(Number of Bands Per Inch for Shadow Effect)

	Agate Weight	Number of Bands	Length Increment	Factor Total Multiplied	Per Inch
1.	1.05 lbs.	70	1.00 inch	1	70
2.	.90 lbs.	107	.25 inch	4	428
3.	.40 lbs.	100	.50 inch	2	200
4.	.25 lbs.	37	.25 inch	4	148
5.	.21 lbs.	88	.25 inch	4	352
6.	` .18 lbs.	225	.50 inch	2	450
7.	.12 lbs.	32	.50 inch	2	64
8.	.07 lbs.	31	.25 inch	4	124
9.	.07 lbs.	54	.50 inch	2	108
10.	.05 lbs.	68	.25 inch	4	272

Range Between 64 and 450

Other Features

The micro-stratigraphy discussed so far includes features that developed during the Lake Superior agate's formation over one billion years ago. Two other common features, on the other hand, developed relatively recently, mainly during glacial transport. On most agates, particularly larger ones, small crescent-shaped fractures called "friction cracks" are common. These cracks were caused by high pressure contact or collisions with other rocks when the agates were transported during the steady advance of the Superior lobe. Because agates have conchoidal fracture, it is natural for these surface cracks to be curved.

The other feature developed during glacial transport in response to the more violent abrasion is the agate's "peeled" texture. The fracturing of the agate in this instance occurred along the banding plane between well-developed individual bands. The result is a smooth, undulating band surface that often "steps down" into other peeled bands. Usually, this exposed band surface becomes heavily oxidized and stained because the iron ions and hematite tends to lie along this plane.

Although this review cannot be considered a comprehensive survey, I hope it indicates some the many interesting and beautiful features within Lake Superior agates that you can discover if you stop and take a closer look.

Essay: Agate Surprises

My passion for the Lake Superior agate and the lore that surrounds it is obviously strong, and has continued to grow. I've come to the conclusion that "agate fever," sometimes called "Agatitis," is a life-long addiction. I know this because I've met many of those afflicted with it.

The one to tell me of the agate "disease" was George Flaim. George, in my opinion, was the greatest Lake Superior agate collector of all time, not only for the beautiful stones he found over the years, or the quality of the stones he acquired through buying and trading, but because of his whole philosophy. He enjoyed not only the beauty of the stones, but sharing that beauty with other people. The agate stories he told me could easily fill another book.

I can't help feeling that my meeting George was somehow meant to be, for he influenced me more than anyone else involved with agates. I first met him on a day when I had gone scuba diving near Gordon, Wisconsin, for an agate a friend claimed to have thrown in a lake. At the time—and since I have not found the agate underwater for the past 23 years—I thought for sure the whole story was a practical joke.

That friend was former Minnesota Vikings Head Coach, Bud Grant. This past summer (2007), I stopped at Bud's house in Bloomington, Minnesota, for his annual garage sale, where he said he had something to show me. Bud explained how that year's drought had lowered the water level in the lake at his cabin to the lowest it had ever been. He said *"I found that agate I threw in the lake."* Thinking he was joking again, I sarcastically said, *"Sure you did."* He then led me into the house, where sitting on the kitchen counter was a softball-sized, multicolored rock. Much to his surprise, the rock turned out *not* to be an agate. I told him it was a rather attractive piece of silicified limestone. The disappointment in his face made me realize that I'd been duped again. After all these years of thinking the story was a practical joke, it turned out his story was true after all!

Bud Grant holds a 6-pound piece of silicified limestone on July 27, 2007, that he thought was a Lake Superior agate he had thrown into a lake decades earlier. Recently, he found the same rock when drought conditions reduced the water level of the lake to a record low.

After I had given up my search for the agate in the lake (back in 1984), I packed my gear back in the car and my friend Mark Brugman and I continued north to Superior, Wisconsin, to check out another large agate. This one, supposedly a 4-pound polished stone, was said to be on display in a drug store. Neither of us had ever seen an agate that big, and our disappointment over the joke played on us earlier in the day made us determined to see this rock.

We located and entered the drug store, but when we inquired about the agate, we were told that it had recently been stolen. Once again we were disappointed. The woman at the counter said that the store manager had owned the agate and might enjoy talking with us. She led us to his office and we introduced ourselves. John Moin was a very nice fellow who sounded pained when he spoke about his stolen agate. It must have been a beauty.

Our conversation shifted to collecting, and he said we should visit a friend of his in Duluth who had some beautiful agates. He told us that his friend's name was George Flaim and that he was a taxidermist who had a shop on the hill overlooking Lake Superior. Intrigued, we got the address and headed over the high bridge to Duluth.

Within half an hour, we found the small shop and pulled into the driveway. We walked up to the side door and knocked. A voice inside said, *"Come on in."* We opened the door and were greeted by a huge stuffed bear with its mouth open wide. As we peered around the room, we could see fish, ducks, moose, and white-tailed deer head lining the walls in various stages of preparation.

In the opposite corner, we saw a man in his early sixties, sitting at a bench painting a fish. We said we were looking for George Flaim, the agate collector. The big, gruff man said, *"That's me."* As we walked across the room toward Mr. Flaim, over and around various animal species, I pulled out a 3-pound agate I had bought at a rock shop in Duluth a month earlier. It was the largest I'd seen at the time, and I readied it for proud display.

I said to Mr. Flaim, *"I understand you collect agates. Have you ever seen one this nice before?"* Without a pause in his brushwork on the fish, he glanced at the stone and chuckled, *"I've owned that rock three different times."* Needless to say, my cocky attitude was squelched in a hurry.

Once I'd regained my composure, we asked him about his agates. He said he had a few, and invited us to visit his home later that afternoon to see some of them. We didn't have any plans, so we accepted his invitation. As we left the shop, I felt confused; I wasn't sure what to think. What did he mean he had owned the rock three times? Was his collection so good that a near-perfect, 3-pound specimen was expendable? My questions were soon to be answered.

Mark and I arrived at George's house at about 3 p.m., and he ushered us into the basement. Upon entering, we sensed a kind of grandeur. As I peered around the room, I could see that the walls were lined with trophy-sized bass and other fish, all of which he had caught. Other specimens and artifacts were of equally high quality. As I thought about the agates again, I nearly shuttered. If his taste in rocks was what I expected, his agates would be awesome.

George offered us chairs and fetched us sodas. We chatted briefly, and then he said, *"You two look like strong boys, go into the back room and bring in the two boxes from inside the vault."* We jumped up and went after the wooden boxes, which looked harmless enough. When we tried to lift them, however, they hardly budged. Determined not to be defeated, we mustered our strength and hauled them in. George then opened the first box and pulled out a rick wrapped in a plastic bag. He handed the bag to me, and I slowly unwrapped it. I still remember that agate, a blood red 1¾-pounder that is still one of my favorites.

We admired the stone, and I thought to myself, *"Can they all be of such quality?"* Much to my astonishment, every agate we examined seemed better than the last. I also began to realize that as we continued to pull agates out, they were gradually getting larger and larger. When we started into the second box, the 20 or so rocks we'd already looked at were strewn about the floor. It was truly an impressive sight.

Eventually, the dream ended as we pulled out the last big agate. It weighed about 7 pounds, and just like the rest, it was a beauty. The final lesson in this agate education came after we'd looked at all the rocks in the boxes. My adrenalin had subsided somewhat, and I was beginning to come back to reality when George got up, went into the back room, and reappeared with a stone that dwarfed everything we'd seen before. It was a 23-pounder, the king of the crowd.

Thinking back to that day, I realize that George must have had fun blowing our minds with his agates. He knew how much we appreciated seeing them. I know what he must have felt, because that's how I feel now when people see my agates.

That special day when I met George changed me forever. I realized then that there's much more to the hobby than just picking and finding agates. Some of the greatest fun is in the experiences shared with others. Trading, buying, and selling can be just as exciting as hunting. In the last 24 years, in addition to collecting agates in the field, I've tracked down numerous collectors to see what they've found and have talked to them about agates. These treasure hunts have been the groundwork for this book, and although it's been hard work, it's also been a series of terrific adventures.

One of the nicest things about traveling around locating fellow agate addicts is that my wife, Janet, has been with me on many of these excursions. Not only has she put up with endless hours of searching for agates in the pits, but she has also endured many repetitions of what non-addicts might find boring stories told by other collectors and myself.

Once in a while, when I become especially obsessed with the stones instead of paying attention to her, she'll refer to the agates as the "other women." Her feeling is common; more than once, I've overheard her and another collector's wife call themselves "agate widows." A cute phrase, but one I think I'd better remember. In spite of all I put her through, I know she'll always be there. The summer we became engaged, Janet surprised me with the greatest gift I could have ever received: a very special rock.

While I was busy buying her a diamond ring, Janet was also busy; she and George were working out a little deal. The weekend after we became engaged, we traveled to Duluth to spend some time together and show off her ring to a few friends. Naturally, we had to show it to George and his wife, Elaine, who thought it was beautiful. Then, just before we left, he and Janet confessed to their little conspiracy, and George handed me the present Janet wanted me to have.

I can't really describe my feelings as I gazed upon the 5¾-pound agate. Of all the agates I saw the day I met George, this was my favorite (see portfolio page C-10). To this day, I still feel that it is one of the finest-quality Lake Superior agates I've ever seen. We call it the "Engagement Agate," and rather than trying to describe it, judge for yourself. Thank you Janet!

CHAPTER 8
Lapidary and Treating Agates

The cutting and polishing of rocks and minerals is an ancient art called "lapidary," a term derived from the Latin word for "stone." Throughout recorded time, many civilizations have used polished stone as currency, jewelry, and works of art. Like many other gemstones, which are often worth comparatively little until they are altered by man, the Lake Superior agate may take on added beauty and value when polished or cut.

Agates, like diamonds, must be individually studied to determine how and where they should be worked to bring out their highest beauty and best optical properties. Criteria to be considered are size, shape, color and quality. These properties determine the type of work to be performed. The following discussion focuses on lapidary techniques and the particular kinds of agates that will best benefit from those techniques.

Probably the most common lapidary technique used on agates is **tumbling**. A tumbler consists of a belt-driven hollow drum containing polishing grit of various sizes. An electric motor slowly rotates the drum and, as it turns, the agates placed inside it tumble in the grit. Over a period of days, this material slowly abrades the gems, exposing their hidden banding. Many newer tumblers have vibrators that, when combined with the steady tumbling action, reduce the time necessary to smooth-finish the gemstones.

Both novice and professional collectors tumble agates, using drums of various sizes. Smaller agates (on the order of 1/2" to 1 1/2" in diameter) are most often tumbled. Larger agates can also be tumbled, but they require larger, more expensive drums and a much longer time to smooth and polish. The completed stones are very pretty and are the reward of an enjoyable and inexpensive hobby.

Another lapidary technique used on agates is **slab cutting**. Cutting an agate into slabs is done with diamond-studded circular saws with blades ranging from 4 to 20 inches in diameter. Larger, poorly exposed rough specimens are best suited for slab cutting. Agates cut into slabs vary in thickness (typically 1/4" to 1"), and items made from them include ashtrays, wind-chimes, tabletops, and cabochons.

Yet another lapidary technique is **cabbing**, which is making **cabochons** or **cabs**, from gemstones cut into ovals or hemispheres and polished, but not faceted. To make a cabochon, a slab is first cut from the desired agate. After the cabochon outline is penciled onto the slab, the rough cabochon is cut from the slab and ground smooth with a grinding wheel. Finally, the shaped cab is polished. Finished cabs can be used to create beautiful rings, belt buckles, and other types of jewelry. Cabbing is a very delicate art, requiring skill and experience to do well.

Another popular technique used on agates is called **face polishing**. Putting a "face" on an agate involves cutting off a portion of the stone, or simply grinding down a desired area of the rough specimen and polishing that surface. The polished face can be straight or curved. Agates of all sizes can be faced, and often a specimen that has been heavily oxidized, which masks much of its internal beauty, is greatly enhanced by facing. These specimens are interesting because most of the agate is left in its natural state, with only one side having a handsomely polished face.

Carving is the rarest of all techniques performed on Lake Superior agates, and presents two specific challenges. First, with a hardness of 7, the only effective media for cutting are diamond tools. Second, if a fracture happens to be in the wrong spot, a four-legged subject can end up with three legs in an instant. My experience has been that rough agates sent to China came back with the best quality carvings. However, patience is required; agates I've had carved took between 6 to 9 months to get back.

An interesting but rarely seen lapidary technique occasionally used on agates is the production of polished **spheres** and **marbles**. These perfectly round gemstones are very beautiful, and require a great deal of skill to produce. The specimen is first cut into a cube; the corners are then cut off and the specimen is ground into a rough sphere. Finally, this "near-sphere" is put into a sphere polishing machine that completes the process.

Spheres are fashioned from homemade machines like the one pictured here.

Because nearly all Lake Superior agates are cracked and fractured to some extent, it is difficult to find specimens suitable for lapidary work. The amount of fracturing in an agate will determine both its value and what lapidary technique should be applied to it.

Unblemished gems with no cracks are extremely rare and valuable. Skilled lapidarists can transform quality agates into polished specimens of unrivaled beauty. If you want to learn about working with agates or other rocks, reading is the best way to start; several books on lapidary techniques are available.

While many fine cut and polished Lake Superior agates are produced by hobbyists, another breed of agate enthusiast deplores the idea of defacing these rare gemstones in any way. These individuals prefer the agate as nature's erosive agents left it. As beautiful as many agates are in their natural state, however, glacial abrasion also left minor imperfections that can be easily removed or disguised. The process known as **treating** is the best way of enhancing an agate's natural beauty without defacing it.

The following steps should be followed when treating a Lake Superior agate to improve its natural appearance. First, when you find or acquire an agate, wash it with water and a scrub brush to remove all dirt, dust, and clay trapped in cracks and depressions. Then remove any calcite from the agate, using a weak solution of hydrochloric acid. The white or colorless calcite is very common, and is deposited as a crust on the agate by cool ground waters passing through glacial deposits. Diluted hydrochloric acid (one part HCL to 4 parts water) reacts with calcite and rapidly dissolves it. Hydrochloric acid can be purchased under the name of muriatic acid at any hardware store or pharmacy. Be very careful when using hydrochloric acid, for in concentrated form it will burn skin and clothing. Always slowly add the acid to the water, rather than the water to the acid, because heat is generated when they are mixed.

After all calcite has been removed, wash off any remaining acid with water and allow the stone to dry completely. The agate will take on a "frosted" appearance, caused by light being diffused within tiny surface cracks. This appearance masks the banding and surfaces features that make the agate desirable. The "frosting" can be eliminated by immersing the stone in mineral or baby oil or by rubbing the oil over the agate's entire surface.

After oiling the agate, some collectors place them in sunlight to heat the stone and allow the oil to seep into the tiny cracks and seal them, eliminating the frosted appearance. After an hour or two of time has elapsed, clean the agate of any remaining oil with a towel or rag. The treated agate will reveal the surface features of banding, husk, pits, crystal impressions, oxidation colors, and clear quartz with a clarity and beauty unrivaled in untreated specimens.

However you choose to enhance the beauty of your agates, whether by lapidary, treating, or both, you will have an interesting and enjoyable hobby. But when you are considering which method to use on a particular agate, always remember to study the stone before beginning your work. This individual consideration is especially important when working with larger agates because of their rarity. Remember too that the external beauty of an agate is often overlooked because of curiosity to uncover the unknown beauty inside. Like an unopened Christmas present, not knowing what is hiding inside an agate is often better than the thrill of exposing its contents.

Essay: Learning Lapidary with John Marshall

I can already hear the groans and see the eyebrows raise in disbelief as people who know me read this essay. They won't believe that "Mr. Rough-is-the-only-way-to-go-with-Lakers" finally broke down and came over to the dark side. Well, it's not quite that drastic a move. I've always appreciated a good-quality, polished agate. The problem is that there are so precious few good-polished Lake Superior agates. The practical problems to polishing Lakers are well known to those with experience on the grinding wheels. The storied glacial history of our precious banded beauties produced a legacy of internal fractures.

For years, I've heard the complaints from friends trying to get just one good polished specimen without fractures. I would just smile to myself and think that they just wouldn't learn that the only good Laker is a rough Laker. Over time, my position softened, as I saw the infrequent fracture-free specimen that was truly beautiful. Arguably the finest, big, polished specimen I've ever seen is "Peanut Butter and Jelly." It might be the most popular agate pictured in my books. Even if the color in the earlier photograph was somewhat off, it is still a fantastic piece and, best of all, it has no fractures.

Who wouldn't want a great piece like that? The irony is that you could cut 10,000 agates and not get one as good. For a long time, this logic served to justify my negative position about polishing. However, I would be forever changed after rolling the dice on a two-pound agate that dared me to cut it. In the spring of 2001, Johnny Harris called me and said he had an agate that nobody wanted, but thought I might like it. He said the stone needed to be cut and that he thought it would be killer. I asked him why he didn't cut it, and he wasn't really sure why. We made arrangements to get together and, when I saw it, I instantly knew what he meant. It was a completely enclosed nodule, with only a couple of tiny windows of red-and-white banding peeking out on each end. I could understand why nobody wanted to gamble on this stone, but something in my gut was fluttering. I talked myself into going for it, and negotiated a price with which both Johnny and I could live with.

I studied the stone for a few days and decided to cut a knob off the top side to get a peek inside. A few years earlier, I had bought a 24"-diameter rock saw from Maynard Green and had cut many Brazilian and Mexican agates. This was the first time that I would cut a Laker this big. I felt a little apprehension as I positioned the stone in the vice and cranked the knob into position in front of the diamond-studded saw blade. I lowered the hood, crossed my fingers, and hit the switch. I winched slightly upon hearing the high-pitched grinding noise, as the saw blade moved against the stone. There was no going back now. It would take about 15 minutes for the saw to cut the stone, so I went back to my office and waited. The saw had automatically turned itself off, and the agate was waiting inside. I turned on the light inside the saw and grabbed the handle. I crossed my fingers again and lifted the hood up. I gazed inside and, to my surprise, it went better than I could have imagined. The red-and-white pattern was striking, and I couldn't help but let out an excited yelp! I had hit a home run!

The "Home Run" agate weighed over two pounds before being cut and gave little clue to the spectacular beauty that was hidden inside.

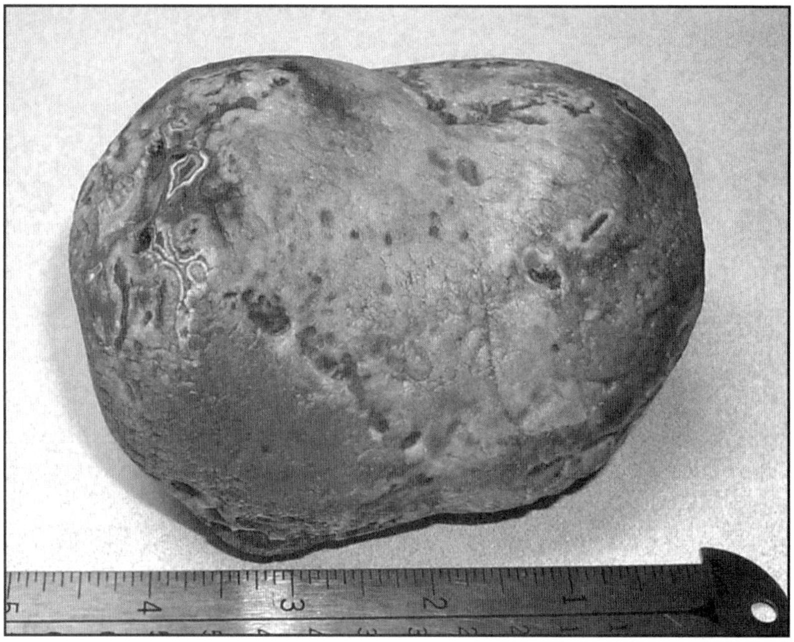

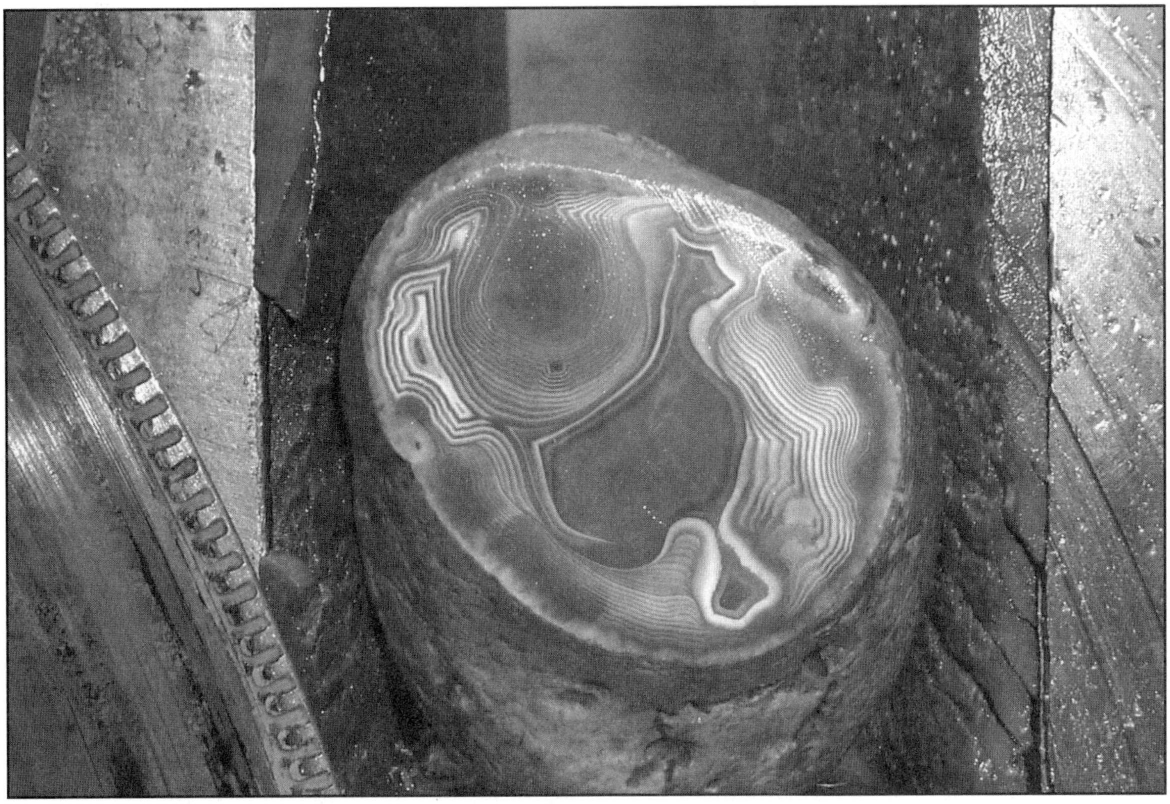

This was the sight my eyes beheld when I opened the hood of the 24" diamond saw and peered in. The two-pound agate I choose to cut and have polished turned out to be a "Home Run."

I pulled the agate from the saw and knew that it deserved the skills of an expert to put the proper polish on its beautiful face. I had two good options and decided to use both. I first sent the stone to Bob Lynch at Agate City in Two Harbors, Minnesota, who put on a great curved face with a high-quality polish. After enjoying the stone for a while, I packed it up and shipped it out to Oregon, where my friend John Marshall was more than happy to apply his "plate-glass" finish to the surface. When the stone returned, I was ecstatic to have benefited from the skills of two of the very best Laker craftsmen.

I suppose it was that experience that ultimately led to my decision to take the plunge. I knew that "Home Run" quality agates were extremely rare, but reasoned it would be nice to be able to polish a stone when I wanted to. I had told myself for years that when I got "older" I would take up polishing. Even though I was only 47 years old, I decided that 2006 was the year to do it. Fortunately for me, both Bob Lynch and John Marshall volunteered to share their skills and experience. In June, I drove up to Two Harbors and picked up the new Titan polishing machine that Bob had sold me. I had built a special bench for my new machine in the basement, and I was now ready to learn the craft.

John and I made plans for him to stay at my house over the week of Moose Lake Agates Days. The plan was for us to work with the new machine in the evenings, so I would be able to get in several hours of prime tutoring from John. It had been several years since John had visited Minnesota, due primarily to health reasons. I wasn't sure he'd even make the trip, but was pleasantly surprised to see his smiling face when I picked him up at the airport. We figured it had been eight years since we'd seen each other, but the conversation flowed on the drive home like no time had elapsed.

I think John was more excited to see my new machine than me. John had sent two boxes before his arrival, with all the necessary items to be a master polisher. I pulled the boxes out, and John opened them and began the lesson. Inside the boxes were latex gloves, paper towels, extra grinding wheels, a marking pen, a large crescent wrench for changing the wheels, and a magnifying lens that attached to the flexible working light for inspecting the stones. The last item John pulled from the box was what he called his secret weapon. It was a plastic bottle filled with a fine, white powder of cerium oxide. He said this was the secret to getting the plate-glass finish.

I was more than ready to get started, and John was just as eager. He began with the 8"-diameter, 80-grit grinding wheel on the far left side. He explained how this wheel was used for the initial shaping of the surface. When it was my turn, I took a small paint-stone we purchased earlier in the day and pressed it against the wheel. I was surprised at how fast the diamond cut away at the stone. It was easier than I thought to shape the surface. We then moved onto the 120-grit wheel, which also cut into the stone, but was much less aggressive. John showed me the technique for grinding out the deeper 80-grit scratches and smoothing out flat spots. Each time we switched wheels, we had to move the portable water sprayer that kept the wheels wet as we ground away. The final wheel on the left side of the motor was the 220-grit sanding wheel. John explained that this was the wheel you spend the most time on, doing the final shaping of the surface and chasing after the coarse scratches. *"This is the wheel that dictates the eventual quality of the final polish,"* John said.

Each time I thought the surface was done, we'd dry off the stone and check for scratches under the magnifying lens, which was conveniently attached to the flexible light. Each time we checked, it seemed like new scratches had appeared. I was beginning to understand why it takes more than skill to be a good polisher; it also takes patience. Once we were satisfied that the scratches were gone, we moved to the wheels on the right side. The next wheel was the 600-grit wheel, which generally takes much less time than the 220 wheel. John cautioned me to be sure to spend time working the edges to ensure the entire surface got finished.

The machine came with a total of six wheels, but John changed the configuration down to five. The final wheel he had shipped in was designed for use with the cerium oxide. John poured the white powder into a plastic cup that had a little water in the bottom, and then mixed it using an old toothbrush. He then applied a coating of the slurry onto the contoured surface of the agate. After making sure the buffing wheel was saturated, he carefully touched the surface. I watched as John slowly worked the entire surface, until the slurry was gone. John cautioned me not to apply too much pressure because that would increase friction and heat up the stone, causing surface cracks. When the process was finished, he sprayed the excess cerium oxide off, and wiped the stone dry. The finished agate was just as John had promised. The polish was so smooth I could read the wattage printed on the light bulb reflecting off the surface. I now knew how to get that "plate-glass" finish.

For the next few days, we worked side by side, polishing both Lakers and Botswana agates. We polished both large- and small-sized agates, periodically switching sides on the machine. I had to laugh at John when he made a makeshift coverall out of a plastic garbage bag. He said it might look silly, but it served its function perfectly. I preferred getting wet from the spray of the pumps and looked even sillier with the wet spot on my clothes suggesting poor bladder control.

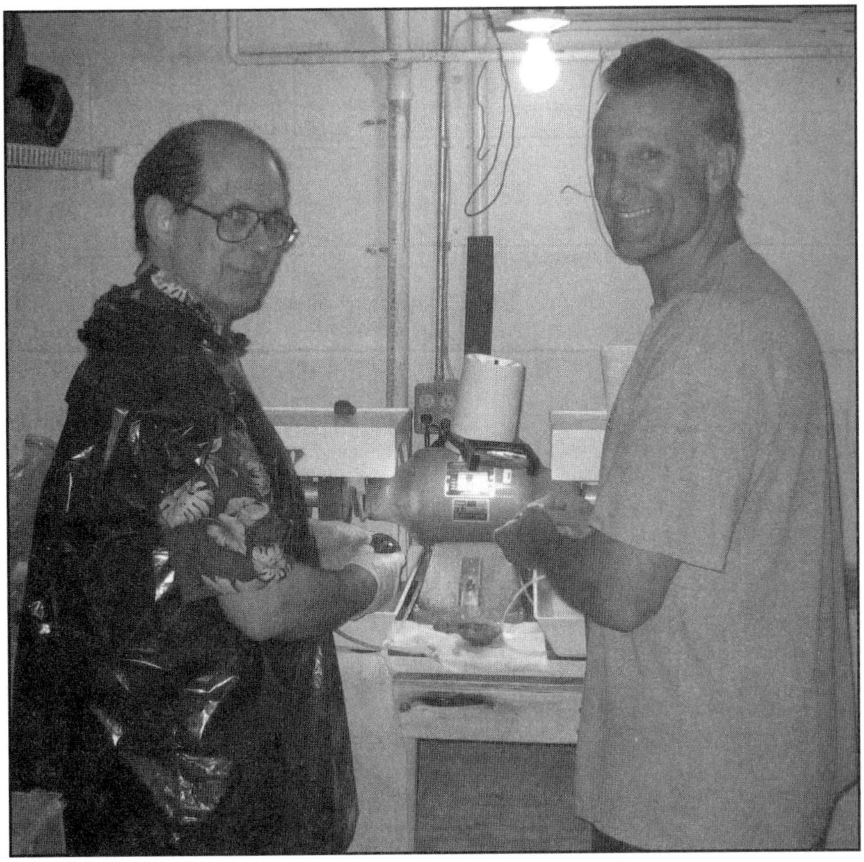

John Marshall and the author pause for a quick snapshot during my agate-polishing education on July 11, 2006. A black plastic garbage bag served as a makeshift coverall for John. Photograph by Grant Wolter.

After spending four nights being coached by John, I felt like I was getting the hang of it. The biggest thing I had to focus on was patience, making sure to—as John would say—"Kill all the scratches" with the 220 sanding wheel. We polished several agates that turned out pretty good; even for a beginner like me. While I still firmly believe that rough Lakers are by far the best, I now have a new appreciation for polished specimens.

The best of the crop of both Botswana and Lake Superior agates that John Marshall and the author polished in July of 2006. The size of the agates (L to R) in pounds is 3.42, 0.36, 0.94, 0.12, 0.78 and 2.68.

Essay: The Minnehaha Falls Agate

Awesome! That's about all I can say as I sat at my kitchen table gazing at what has to be the most incredible Lake Superior agate I have ever seen. The people that know me best would roll their eyes and say, *"I've heard that before."* No doubt I've fawned over many beautiful agates in the past. But this agate transcends all the rest. Not only does this specimen have the qualities of the absolute best, but it has something that no other Laker I have ever seen has: proof of association with Native Americans.

Before I share the history of the agate, let me describe what role Mother Nature played in producing this magnificent specimen. First at 7.39 pounds, it's a giant in the world of Lake Superior agates. Second, the color can only be described as perfect. It has the classic brunt red and white color, typical of many Lakers. The shape of the stone is as good as a person could ask for.

Many years ago I remember hearing about the "Minnehaha Falls" agate. I recall the shape being described as bread loaf-like with pattern coming out both ends. An agate like that would be terrific, but the actual shape is even better. The agate is somewhat box-shaped with glacially rounded corners. It rests on a relatively flat, peeled side and sits like an equi-dimensional nodule with a slightly domed top. The agate's exterior is composed of roughly 1/4 original husk, 1/3 glacially washed peeled texture and the remainder is a myriad of large and small faces.

The first large face is rectangular in shape along one side of the stone. The left side of this pattern pinches into a channel that runs vertical into a larger triangular shaped face covering the top. The largest face has fat white bands starting at the husk. The agate becomes a floater toward the center of the face with excellent contrast between the sugar quartz and mostly red bands. Without anything else, this agate easily stands as one of the best ever. However, there is more!

As is always my practice, I try to learn as much of the known history of a special agate as I can. A sheet of paper that came with the agate said it was found at Minnehaha Falls in 1932. These falls are a beautiful area along Minnehaha Creek near where it flows into the Mississippi river in South Minneapolis. My research revealed that Native Americans considered the area around the falls sacred. It is believed that for centuries the Minnehaha Falls area was frequented by Native Americans with many rituals performed at the beautiful spot. Many ancient burial mounds are located near the falls. One can only wonder how many people worshiped this site over the centuries.

In 1932, a rock-hound walking along the bank of the creek, below the falls, found the agate in the mud. Little is known of the lucky individual, for he wanted his identity to remain a secret. The discoverer kept the agate for 29 years until he sold it to George Bullock in 1961. George displayed the agate at many rock shows between 1962 and 1975.

Over the years, many of my rock-hound friends have told me about the Minnehaha Falls agate and have tried to describe it. None of them remembered seeing it after the middle 1970s. George relayed that he stopped showing the agate and eventually sold it to his friend Stan Sivertson in 1983. Stan passed away in 1988 and his wife Carol had the agate until now.

From the first days of my seriously collecting agates in the early 1980s, I had heard about the "Falls" agate. I first learned that the agate was located in March of 1995 and might be for sale. Unfortunately, I didn't have an address or phone number of the owner. What I did know was that the woman who had it lived somewhere in Minneapolis. It drove me crazy knowing the agate was so near yet so far away.

Finally, after a great deal of detective work, I was able to get her phone number. I could feel that I was getting closer to seeing the fabled agate I'd heard about for so long. It was now the middle of July and I was riddled with excitement as I dialed the number. The phone at the other end rang and rang and rang. I thought I might have the wrong number and tried again. There was no answer. I dialed the number at least a dozen times over the next few days. To say I was frustrated is an understatement. Eventually, I decided to call once in the morning and in the afternoon every Tuesday. This routine continued into August with still no answer. By then I was almost ready to quit.

On a late August Saturday, I was completely exasperated and asked my wife, Janet, what I should do. She suggested I call and let the phone ring once, hang up and then dial again. It sounded like a good idea to me. I dialed the number, but accidentally let it ring twice before I hung up. I cursed myself for being so careless but dialed the number again anyway. It rang a couple of times and then guess what…? She answered! I was so shocked I almost didn't know what to say. I didn't want long though, and quickly got acquainted.

Eventually we talked about why she wouldn't answer the phone. She said she had many harassing calls and, therefore, had set up a system where her mother would call and let the phone ring twice and then call again. We both laughed when I told her how I accidentally broke the code.

Carol let me know that she was interested in selling the agate, but she wasn't in any hurry. After three long months, she finally decided to sell the stone. I'm grateful she selected my family to be the new caretakers. At last the precious gem was in my hands. I now had the opportunity to study the "groove" I had heard so much about.

The agate had a linear groove that circled the stone through roughly the center. This shallow (~1/4" deep) trench was definitely not produced by glacial abrasion. The groove instead, was purposefully made by human hands.

After visiting with experts of Native American artifacts, they believed the agate was used as a ceremonial piece. At over seven pound, the agate was probably too big to be used as a hand-held weapon or tool. Also, the agate does not show evidence of impact consistent with these types of instruments. The groove is rough and was probably fashioned by pecking with another stone. If the stone had been used as an axe or hammer the groove would have been smooth. A smooth groove would be produced by wet leather being rubbed across the stone with sand. The Minnehaha Falls agates' groove was definitely rough and consistent with impact pecking.

How the agate got to that spot in the mud on the bank of the creek, we will never know. The number of people who have gazed upon the gemstone since it was plucked for the creek bank probably represents only a fraction of the number of humans that once enjoyed and perhaps worshiped this rarest of agate gemstones.

CHAPTER 9
Appraising Lake Superior Agates

Probably the most commonly asked question of me by people who have found an agate and are thinking of selling it is this: *How much money is my agate worth?* Although there isn't an official standardized method for appraising Lake Superior agates, or any other type of agate, there is a general industry standard for valuing agates that starts at about 50 cents a pound for small (1"-sized and smaller), unsorted, tumbling-grade material. The price goes up from there for bulk agate to as high as 10 dollars a pound for larger (¼-pound or larger), high-quality grade, rough agate.

Assigning a value to larger-sized collector-grade agates can vary anywhere from 10 dollars a pound to as much as a $1,000 a pound, which is retail pricing, for the absolute best, high-quality, large specimens. One has to remember there is a difference between wholesale and retail values. Dealers typically buy agate in bulk or as collections at up to 50% of the retail value. The biggest problem with assigning a value is the high subjectivity of what constitutes quality in an agate between appraisers. What I'd like to try to do is introduce a system that quantifies various aspects of Lake Superior agates to help appraisers determine a fair market value.

Size

For a long time, size was the primary factor in determining an agate's value. Size is very important, and after about one pound, the value goes up exponentially, due to rarity as size or weight increases. The following numerical scale reflects the relative rarity (and value) according to size:

Weight in Pounds	Rating
< 0.5	**1**
0.5 to 1.0	**2**
1.0 to 2.0	**3**
2.0 to 3.0	**4-5**
3.0 to 5.0	**6-7**
> 5.0	**8-10**

Shape

Shape	Rating
Highly angular with sharp edges	1-2
Irregular with rough edges	3-4
Irregular with smooth edges	5-6
Oval or flat with rough surfaces	7
Oval with smooth surfaces	8-9
Oval or round water-washed	10

Color

Color	Rating
Light to dark gray	1-2
Yellow (limonite staining)	3
Rusty red & orange	4-5
Dull red and white	6-7
Multi-colored "paint"	8
Bright red and white	9-10

Banding (includes quality of eye, tube, sagenite, etc.)

Banding	Rating
Undifferentiated	1-2
Weak or poorly defined	3-4
Fine to thick with low contrast	5-6
Fine to thick with medium contrast	7-8
Fine to thick with high contrast	9-10

Composition & Contrast

C & C	Rating
Broken or badly chipped	1-2
Mostly peeled and rough	3-4
Mostly peeled and smooth	5-6
Open, rolling pattern with husk	7-8
Complete fortification pattern with husk	9-10

Quartz

Quartz	Rating
Greater than 75%	**1-2**
50% to 75%	**3**
25% to 50%	**4-5**
0 to 25% (Solid Plug)	**6-7**
0 to 25% (Floater)	**8-9**
0% (Solid Agate)	**10**

In theory, once an agate has been rated according to the six categories, the assigned numerical total will help in determining a value to the agate.

I'm sure there are people who are asking, *"How do you evaluate other types of agates like tube, eye, moss, etc.?"* These categories are more subjective, but the same criteria can be applied to these varieties as well. When it is all said and done, this information serves simply as a guide. How much an agate is worth is in the eye of the beholder, and, of course, the seller. Most often it boils down to the age-old axiom in sales that says an agate is worth what someone is willing to pay for it!

In case any of you readers are interested in having your agates appraised, I am a licensed geologist (Minnesota License #30024) and perform professional written appraisals. Give me a call or send me an email if you are interested or have any questions: swolter@amengtest.com (612-875-7871 or 651-659-1345).

Essay: The Top Ten Polished Lake Superior Agates

While digging through my old agate files during the writing of this edition, I found some interesting things. One of those was the hand-written notes and Top Ten list (of rough Lake Superior agates) of the now-deceased legendary Laker collector and my good friend, George Flaim. Back in 2000, while writing my other agate book entitled, *"The Lake Superior Agate: One Man's Journey,"* I decided to come up with a Top Ten list of the greatest rough Lake Superior agates of all time. I sent out surveys to several long-time collectors, who all seemed to enjoy picking out their all-time favorite agates and ranking them.

George was no exception, and after reading through those lists, I decided to reproduce his list at the end of this essay to give you a flavor for the wise man with a great sense of humor that many of us got to know so well. Several agates on his list are pictured in this book as well, but to see the entire final Top Ten list, you'll have to read my other book!

Because the Top Ten list of *rough* agates generated so much interest and discussion, I decided to do another Top Ten list for this edition; only this time it's the top ten *polished* Lake Superior agates.

The protocol was to ask (via email) for any and all interested collectors to nominate specimens to be considered. The only stipulation was the agates had to be larger than 12 ounces in size. Specimens could be either tumbled or face polished. The voting panel was limited to individuals who had been involved in the hobby for at least a decade, and had experience polishing Lakers. The judges were asked to rank their top ten in order from 1 to 10. Each agate's ranking was equivalent to points, and just like the game of golf, the winner had the lowest point total.

Our panel of judges included Charlie White, Jennifer and Gary Pitoscia, John Harris, Bill Steffes, Mike Carlson, Bruce Peddle, and me. Before getting started, we agreed that the beautiful agates from the Upper Peninsula of Michigan and Michipocotin Island were in a different category, and decided not to include them in the competition. Everyone brought agates along, which included four that made the final list. What surprised everyone was how different people's opinions were regarding what constituted a great polished agate. I personally thought there were four or five agates that didn't make the final cut that were better than the agates that did. One of the problems for all of us was trying to evaluate an agate from a photograph. In general, the agates that were present did much better than those that were not. However, the agate chosen number one was judged from a photo, so go figure! All in all, it was a fun competition, with many great agates submitted. There no doubt are many other great polished agates out there that could have made this list, but for now, here are that Top Ten polished Lake Superior agates, as selected by our distinguished panel:

10. **"George's Paint Stone"** (1.43 lbs.) – A beautiful peanut butter-orange and white stunner.

9. **"Bill's Baby"** (0.88 lbs.) – Blood red and white beauty with high contrast and flawless polish.

8. **"Lynch's Lunker"** (1.33 lbs.) – A flawless, fine-banded beauty with great shadow.

7. **"Smart Agate"** (4.15 lbs.) – This fantastic tumble-polished stone was found by Charlie Smart near Pillager, Minnesota, in the early 1960s, but hasn't been seen since.

6. **"Maynards Agate"** (2.65 lbs.) – An eye-popper from across the room, with a beautifully busy pattern.

5. **"Home Run"** (2.27 lbs.) – Classic red and white colors with an eye-catching face.

4. **"Charlie's Pride"** (1.25 lbs.) – Rich dark colors with a large, flawless face.

3. **"Smile Agate"** (3.25 lbs.) – Stunning bright and bold pattern and colors with a large face.

2. **"Peanut Butter and Jelly"** (2.24 lbs.) – A long-time fan favorite with rare colors and a fracture-free face.

1. **"Classic Quality"** (2.09 lbs.) – Bright, bold, and symmetric pattern that represents the classic beauty of Lake Superior agates.

To see color photographs of these great agates see portfolio pages C-27 to C-32.

Eight experienced Lake Superior agate collectors gathered to vote for the Top Ten *polished* Lake Superior agates at the author's home on March 9, 2008. Left to right: Bill Steffes, Jennifer and Gary Pitoscia, Scott Wolter, John Harris, Mike Carlson, and Charlie White. (Photograph by Janet Wolter)

Scott: Every time I go over this, the No 1 agate Spot comes out as a tie. I can't think of it; any other way, at all!!

Top Ten Agates Of All Time

\# (1) ENGAGEMENT Comments BOTH FOR EXTERIOR CONDITION - COLOR - SIZE + OVERALL

\# (1) PAISLEY PARK (PAINT) COVERAGE OF BANDING

2. CAMPFIRE 6# Comments CONFIRMATION OF SHAPE COLOR ARRAINGEMENT AND MAJESTY OF DISPLAY

3. JINGLE BELLS Comments JUST ABOUT UNBELIEV-EABLE - ARRAINGEMENT OF EXTERNAL HUSK PATTERNS

4. HAROLD JOHNSON Comments THIS SHOULD RATE HIGER BUT IS JUST A PARTIAL STONE - FOR COLOR AND WHITENESS COULD BE NO I.

5. BLUE SADGE 1¼# Comments J. MARSHALL - THE GREAT-EST BLUE I EVER SEEN. RARE + GORGEOUS. THERE CAN'T BE TWO.

6. DAUGHERTY 3½# Comments JUST PERFECT IN ALL RESPECTS. IF YOU CAN'T LIKE THIS ONE, YOU HATE YOURSELF.

7. TRACY'S AGATE 4½# Comments NOT A MAR OR SCRATCH ON THE STONE - IT NEVER TOUCHED ANOTHER STONE - GORGEOUS

8. JAN'S 5# RED Comments OUT OF THIS WORLD IN SHAPE COLOR. THE DISPLAY ATTITUDE CANNOT BE BEAT

9. WRIGHTS WATER WASH 1¾ Comments - NOTHING I CAN SAY - FOR GOSH-SAKE TAKE TIME + LOOK AT IT. UNBELIEVEABLE WATER WASH

10. ________ Comments ________

I have a strong feeling that "our Lord" made my two No 1 stones for himself.

Always deep respect for all agates,

George Flaim.

(over)

During the 2001 voting for the Top Ten *rough* Lake Superior agates, collector and judge, George Flaim, wrote a humorous and well thought-out list that included some insightful comments.

This year marks my 61st year in agates. At the ripe age of 15 years old and the year of 1937, I started picking pea size agates on the railroad grades coming out of the Minnowa pit in Virginia Mn. At this year everyone was trying to recover from the great depression of 1929. Kids never had any money and most of them had for example 5 cents each to celebrate 4th of July, I would get all the empty ink bottles from our art classes + fill them with these gorgeous pea size water-washed agate stones and sell them for 10¢ each. Also bottles full of Iron pyrite for 10¢ each. 1936 + 37 were the dry years. Over 5,000 lakes in Minn. went completly dry. So did the farmers wells. An adult would lower me into the dry wells on a board and rope and I woued pick the pyrite out of the clean sand. For 3 months we thought it was real gold, imagine the let-down. At the age of 76 years old I can say; I started out tough and will go out tough.

A washed out monster!

Pay respect to all Lakers.

George Flaim was one of the truly colorful characters who assembled one of the finest collections ever over the course of his 62 years in the Lake Superior agate hobby.

Essay: The Wildest Picker

One of the toughest things I've had to deal with while picking occurs because of my competitive nature. When picking with other people, there is a silent, or sometimes not-so-silent, competition as to who will find the biggest and best agate. In addition to my own experiences, I've heard some great tales about competition in the pits. One of the best stories I've heard was told by-who else?-George Flaim.

On a trip to Duluth many years ago, I spent an evening with George talking about this book. I told him I was interested in writing about some of the personalities I'd met through agate collecting. George sat back, chucked to himself, and said, *"Kid, there's one guy you should have met."* I prodded him for the story and over the next hour he told me about the late Chauncey Wheeler, in George's opinion the wildest picker whoever lived.

After he had filled me in on Chauncey's background, and about the years they had picked together, he began to tell about one day in the pits he said he'd never forget...

I had rained 2 1/2" the night before and George, Chauncey, and an 80-year-old friend named Abel Oinonin arose before dawn for an all-day agate hunt. The time was early spring in 1969 and there was still snow on the ground in a few places, but they selected a few pits outside Duluth where they thought they might find some big agates.

Shortly after lunch, Chauncey was walking along the drop at one of pits when he spotted what looked to be a big agate. Chauncey was a very superstitious person, and he had developed a habit of performing a strange ritual anytime he or anyone else with him discovered an agate weighing more than a pound. He would not let anyone touch the agate until everyone in his party had expressed appreciation for the find. His ritual consisted of sitting down next to the agate, lighting a cone of incense he carried with him, and *"paying homage to the lord of the pits."* As crazy as this sounds, George insists it was true. He said, *"The bigger the agate, the longer the homage period was,"* adding, *"If an agate over 2 pounds was found, forget about picking for a while. You could count on a half hour to 45 minutes of homage."*

When George saw the agate Chauncey had discovered, he realized that if he got caught up in the ritual, he would waste choice picking time. This time, George thought, *"Forget it."* So, although Abel politely sat down next to Chauncey, George kept right on looking for agates. While his friends were honoring what turned out to be a 1 1/2-pound agate, George found three big agates, each weighing more than 3 pounds! At the end of the day, they had a picture taken of the three of them, each holding one of the big agates. It seems somehow appropriate that Chauncey has his hand and the largest agate (4 pounds, 4 ounces) out of the picture. It just wasn't Chauncey's day.

Proud pickers pose after an especially successful day in the pits. Left to right: George Flaim, Abel Oinonin, and Chauncey Wheeler.

CONCLUSION

I hope this book has taught you something about the Minnesota State gemstone as well as given you some enjoyment. Above all, I hope that some of my readers will be inspired to take up agate collecting. I can't begin to express all the pleasure I've had over the past 25 years, and the fun I look forward to in the future as I continue collecting. It appears that the hobby has indeed flourished once again and there are still countless big and beautiful Lake Superior agates out there to be discovered for many years to come. All that is needed is people with a desire to find them.

Happy hunting!

GLOSSARY

Abrasion – Scraping action induced by glacial processes; also the tumbling action of streams and beaches.

Accessory Mineral – The mineral constituents of a rock that occurs in such small amounts that they are disregarded in its classification and definition.

Agate – A waxy variety of cryptocrystalline quartz in which the colors occur in bands, clouds or distinct groups.

Aggie ball (slang) – A relatively round agate, usually small, with no banding or internal features visible.

All-timer (slang) - An agate of exceptional quality, very rare and valuable.

Amethyst – A purple or bluish-violet variety of quartz used as a gem.

Amygdule – A gas cavity or vesicle in volcanic rocks, filled with secondary products such as zeolites, calcite, and silica minerals.

Basalt – Dark volcanic rock comprised of fine-grained minerals.

Bleached agate – Whitening or loss of color due to prolonged exposure to sunlight.

Botryoidal texture – Natural habit of crystal growth resembling the form of a bunch of grapes.

Calcite ($CaCO_3$) – One of the most common minerals; the principal constituent of limestone.

Candy Striper (slang) – An agate with predominantly bold red and white colored banding.

Carbon dioxide (CO_2) – A colorless, odorless, nonpoisonous gas that is a minor but normal part of ambient air.

Cenozoic – The latest of the four eras of geologic time, extending from the close of the Mesozoic (65 million years ago) to the present.

Chalcedony – Cryptocrystalline quartz, the mineral of agate and chert.

Chatoyance – Having a luster resembling the changing luster of the eye of a cat, generally a property of translucent materials containing parallel fibrous structures capable of scattering light.

Colloid – A state which exists between a true solution and a suspension, and arises because the particles are so small (1-10 microns) that the electrical and other forces which tend to support them in the dispersion medium are greater then the gravitational forces tending to cause them to settle.

Composition – An aggregate, mixture, mass, or body formed by combining two or more substances; the chemical constituents of a rock or mineral; the mineralogical constitution of a rock.

Conchoidal fracture – A rock type or mineral fracture giving smoothly curved surfaces, characteristic of quartz.

Cross-section – A profile portraying an interpretation of a vertical section of the earth explored by geophysical or geological methods.

Crystal impression – A mold or cast left protruding into an agate, usually made by calcite before agate formation.

Crystalization – The process through which crystalline phases separate from a gas, liquid solution, or rigid solution.

Decorative stone – Rock used in landscaping adorning homes, businesses, etc.

Deposition – The precipitation of mineral matter from solution as the deposition of agate or vein quartz.

Drift – Any rock material, such as boulders, till, gravel, sand or clay, transported by a glacier and deposited by or from the ice, or in water derived from the melting of the ice.

Drop – Accumulation of rock at the base of a gravel pit wall or bank.

Erosion – The group of processes by which earthy or rock material is loosened or dissolved and removed from any part of the earth's surface.

Ettringite – ($Ca_6A_{12}(SO_4)_3(OH)_{12}$ – 26 H_2O) A common hydration mineral product of Portland cement that typically forms within the cement paste.

Eye – The perfectly round, circular banded pattern found on some agates.

Face – A term applied to a well exposed banded area on an agate.

Field stone – (slang) Glacially deposited gravel and rock exposed at the surface.

Fill hole – That area or areas where solutions entered and exited the vesicle.

Floating bands – Bands of chalcedony bound on both sides by clear crystal quartz.

Fortification – A term applied to pattern of agate banding often resembling the enclosing nature of a fort.

Fracture – The manner of breaking and appearance of a mineral when broken, which is distinctive for certain minerals.

Frost action – The weathering process caused by repeated cycles of freezing and thawing.

Gelatin – Jellylike material formed by coagulation of colloidal dispersion.

Gemstone – A general term for any precious or semiprecious stone.

Geode – A hollow, globular body, with an interior lining of inward-projecting crystals.

Glacier – A mass of ice with definite lateral limits, with motion in a definite direction and originating from the compacting of snow by pressure.

Holocene – Recent, that period of time since the last ice age.

Husk (slang) – A general term applied to the unabraded exterior of an agate.

Hydrostatic pressure – The pressure exerted by water at any given point in a body of water at rest.

Interbedded – Occurring between beds, or lying in a bed parallel to other beds of a different material.

Iris – The rainbow effect sometimes produced when sunlight is refracted through a thinly cut slab of agate.

Iron-oxide – Any mineral containing iron (Fe) and oxygen (O), including hematite (Fe_2O_3), magnetite (Fe_3O_4), goethite (FeOOH), and limonite.

Juvenile waters – Water that is derived from the interior of the earth and has not previously existed as atmospheric or surface water.

Lacy banding – The undulating pattern of chalcedony bands deposited over the tops of quartz crystals within an agate.

Lapidary – A skilled work of cutting and polishing gems or other stones.

Laurentide ice sheet – A mass of continental ice centered, during the Pleistocene Epoch, over what is now Hudson Bay.

Limonite – A mineral; field term for a group of brown, amorphous, naturally occurring, hydrous ferric minerals.

Magma – A molten rock, formed within the crust or the upper mantle of the earth, which may consolidate to form an igneous rock.

Manganese oxide – Any mineral containing manganese (Mn) and oxygen (O).

Meltwaters – Rivers and streams of melted glacial ice.

Mesozoic – An era ranging in time from 230 to 65 million years ago, a duration of 165 million years.

Microstratigraphy – Microscopic features within agates.

Mineral – A structurally homogenous solid of definite chemical composition formed by the inorganic processes of nature.

Moss Agate – A variety of agate containing solid moss-like masses of manganese-oxides entombed by massive or banded chalcedony.

Original banding – Exposed banding unaltered by weathering or oxidation.

Outwash – Drift deposited by meltwater streams beyond active glacier ice.

Overburden – A general term for all glacial deposits including till, moraine, outwash, etc.; also regolith, alluvium, etc. in unglaciated areas.

Oxidation – A process of combining with oxygen; removal of one of more electrons from an ion or an atom.

Painted agate – a heavily oxidized and stained agate that appears painted.

Paleozoic - An era ranging in time from 600 to 225 million years ago, a duration of 375 million years.

Paradise Beach agate – A type of agate originating from Paradise Beach location on the North Shore of Lake Superior, in Minnesota. Many contain small stringers of copper.

Peeled agate (slang) – An agate with fracturing between bands along the banding plane.

Percussion cracks – Crescent-shaped cracks caused by violent contact with other rocks, on rocks with conchoidal fracture.

Permeable – Having a texture that permits water to move through it perceptively under the head differences ordinarily found in sub-surface water.

Pick (slang) - To hunt for agates.

Pleistocene – The earlier of two epochs comprising the Quaternary Period.

Pit (slang) – Any depression on the husk of agate; also used to mean gravel pit.

Precambrian – All rocks formed more than 600 million years ago.

Quartz (SiO_2) – A mineral; one of the most common mineral on earth.

Quartz ball (slang) An agate composed primarily of clear crystal quartz.

Quaternary Period - The most recent time period, beginning 2 million years ago and continuing into the present.

Rifting event – The formation of a deeper fracture or break in the earth where magma upwellings occur together with spreading along the rift and the creation of new volcanic rock.

Rough stone (slang) – An untreated, unpolished agate.

Sagenite - An acicular variety of rutile occurring in groups of crystals crossing at 60 degrees and often enclosed in quartz or other minerals.

Similar banding – A group of two or more bands of the same thickness and composition.

Shadow agate – A type of agate that exhibits the optical effect created by the perception of depth between parallels bands of chalcedony.

Skin (slang) – Another name for the intact surface of the agate that was in direct contact with the host lava; the husk.

Skong (slang) – To acquire agates through collecting in the field, trading or buying from other collectors.

Smoky quartz – A smoky, black- to brown-colored crystalline variety of quartz caused by exposure to natural radiation.

Solid agate (slang) – An agate banded completely with no clear quartz present.

Spherical – Shape of a fragment approaching the form of a sphere.

Stain (slang) – Refers to color due to oxidation of iron-minerals.

Stratified – Formed or lying in beds, layers or strata.

Stringer – A narrow vein or irregular filament of mineral traversing a rock mass of different material.

Sugar quartz (slang) – A term for clear macrocrystalline quartz named for its sugary appearance.

Superior lobe – The lobe of ice that followed the depression or trough of Lake Superior into Minnesota, carrying Lake Superior agates.

Till – Unsorted debris deposited directly from glacial ice.

Topography – The physical feature of a district or region, the relief and contour of the land.

Translucence – Admitting the passage of light, but not transparent.

Treated (slang) – An agate that has been altered in appearance without physically defacing or removing any material.

Truncating bands – Banding that is pinched so fine as to appear cut off.

Tube agate – A variety of agate with usually parallel, linear projections of mineral matter into the vesicle.

Tumble – To polish agates inside rotating drum with polishing grit.

Vesicle – A small cavity in an igneous rock, formed by the expansion of a bubble of gas or stream during the solidification of the rock.

Volcanic - Produced, influenced, or changed by a volcano or by volcanic processes.

Washout - Small-scale exposure of gravel and rock washed out by rain or melt-water.

Water-level agate - A variety with flat parallel banding topped with a fortification pattern or clear quartz.

Weathering - The group of processes, such as the chemical action of air, rainwater, plants and bacteria in addition to the mechanical action of changes of temperature, whereby rocks on exposure to the weather change in character, decay, and finally crumble into soil.

Wisconsin Glaciation - The last of the four classical glacial stages in the Pleistocene in North America.

BIBLIOGRAPHY

Arnoth, Josef, *Achate: Bilder Im Stein* Switzerland: Buchverlag Basler Zeitung/Birkhauser AG, 1986.

Audubon Society, *Field Guide to North America Rocks and Minerals*, New York: Knopf, 1978.

Bailey, R. H., *Glacier*, Planet Earth Series, Alexandria, Virginia: Time-Life Books, 1982.

Banion, E. L., "The Glaciers and Lake Superior Agates in Kansas", *Lapidary Journal*, [April, 1971], pp. 122-152.

Blair, J. M., "Agate", *Rocks and Minerals*, 11:9 1936, pp. 160-64.

Carlson, Michael, R., *"The Beauty of Banded Agates: An Exploration of Agates from Eight Major Worldwide Sites"*, Fortification Press, Edina, Minnesota, 2002.

Charlton, W., *Ice Ages*, Planet Earth Series, Alexandria, Virginia: Time-Life Books, 1983.

Clark, Roger, *"Fairburn Agate: Gem of South Dakota",* Silverwind Agates, Appleton, Wisconsin, 2002.

Craddock, C., "Late Precambrian Geological Setting", *Geology of Minnesota: A Centennial Volume,* e.d. P. K. Sims and G. B. Morey, pp. 281-291, St. Paul: Minnesota Geological Survey, 1972.

Cross, Brad, *"The Agates of Northern Mexico",* Edina, Minnesota: Burgess Publishing, 1996.

Dietrich, R. V., *Rocks and Minerals*, New York: John Wiley and Sons, 1979.

Editors of Time-Life Books, *Volcano*, Planet Earth Series, Alexandria, Virginia: Time-Life Books, 1982.

Fallick, A. E., J. Jocelyn, T. Donnelly, M. Guy, and C. Behan, "Origins of Agates in Volcanic Rocks from Scotland", Nature [February, 1985].

Flint, R. F., *Glacial and Quaternary Geology*, New York: John Wiley and Sons, 1971.

Hurlbut, C. S. Jr. and C. Klein, *Manual of Mineralogy*, 19th Edition (after J. D. Dana), New York: John Wiley and Sons, 1977.

Iler, R. K., *The Chemistry of Silica*, New York: John Wiley and Sons, 1979.

Jones, F. T., "Iris Agate", *Gem and Gemology*, 20:1 (1966), pp. 10-12.

Krauskopt, K. B., "Dissolution and Precipitation of Silica at Low Temperatures", n.v.n.,n.d.,n.p.

Landmesser, Michael, "Mobility by Metastability: Silica Transport and Accumulation a Low Temperatures", *Geochemistry*, [March, 1995], pp. 149-176.

Landmesser, Miichael, "Structural Characteristics of Agate and Their Significance", *Stuttgart*, [August, 1988], pp. 223-235.

Laufer, Berthold, *Agate: Physical Properties and Origin*, Chicago, Illinois: Field Museum of natural History, 1927.

Leiper, H., *The Agates of North America*, San Diego: Lapidary Journal, 1966.

Mackenzie, F. T. and R. Geis, "Quartz: Synthesis at Surface Conditions", *Science 173* (1971), pp. 533-534.

Macpherson, Dr. H. G., *Agates*, London: British Museum of Natural History/National Museum of Scotland, 1989.

Marshall, John, "Formation of Agate and Chalcedony", *Lapidary Journal*, [August, 1965], pp. 606-607.

Marshall, John, *"The **Other** Lake Superior Agates",* Llao Rock Publications, Beaverton, Oregon, 2006.

Mason, B. and L. G. Berry, *Elements of Mineralogy*, San Francisco: W. H. Freeman, 1968.

Matsch, C. L., *North America and The Great Ice Age*, New York: McGraw-Hill, 1976.

Miller, R., *Continents in Collision*, Planet earth Series, Alexandria, Virginia: Time-Life Books, 1983.

Moltara, A. R. Crespi, and G. Liborio, *Simon & Schuster's Guide to Rocks and Minerals*, New York: Simon & Schuster, 1978.

Ojakangas, R. W. and C. L. Matsch., *Minnesota's Geology*, Minneapolis: University of Minnesota, 1982.

Pabian, R. K. and A. Zarins, "Banded Agates: Origin and Inclusions," University of Nebraska-Lincoln, *Educational Circular No 12*, [June, 1994] 32 pages.

Pabian, R. K., "Lake Superior Agates: A Historical Review." Lapidary Journal, 34:1 (1980), pp. 110-52.

Quick, Lelande, *The Book of Agates*, Philadelphia, Pennsylvania: Chilton Company, 1963.

Sharp, R. P., *Glacier,* Condon Lectures, Eugene: Oregon State System of Higher Education, 1960.

Shaub, B. M., *The Origin of Agates, Thundereggs and Other Nodular Structures*, Northampton, Massachusetts: The Agate Publishing Co., 1989.

Sukow, W. W., "Inside Lake Superior Agates, Part I; The Microscopic Arborescent Copper Inclusions," *Lapidary Journal*, [January, 1987], pp. 50-56.

Sukow, W. W., "Learn How Lake Superior Agates are Formed." *Rock and Gem*, [May, 1996], pp. 28-33.

Vanasse, T. C., *Lake Superior Agate.* Spring Valley: Spring Valley Sun, 1949, 1950, 1956 & 1958.

Wolter, Scott F., *"Ettringite: Cancer of Concrete",* Outernet Publishing, Eden Prairie, Minnesota, 1997.

Wolter, Scott F., "The Lake Superior Agate", Lake Superior Agate Inc., Minneapolis, Minnesota, 1986.

Wolter, Scott F., "The Lake Superior Agate: Second Edition", Burgess Publishing, Edina, Minnesota, 1994.

Wolter, Scott F., "The Lake Superior Agate: Third Edition", Outernet Publishing L.L.C., Eden Prairie, Minnesota, 1996 & 2001.

Wolter, Scott F., "The Lake Superior Agate: One Man's Journey", Outernet Publishing, Eden Prairie, Minnesota, 2001.

Zenz, Johann, *"Agates",* Bode Verlag GmbH, Haltern, Germany, 2005.